A Handbook of Textiles

GW00676410

A Handbook of Textiles

Third Edition

Ann M. Collier

ARNOLD-WHEATON

The Educational Publishing Division of Pergamon Press

Arnold-Wheaton
The Educational Publishing Division of Pergamon Press
Dewsbury Road, Leeds LS11 5TD
and Hennock Road, Exeter EX2 8RP

Pergamon Press Ltd
Headington Hill Hall, Oxford OX3 0BW

Pergamon Press Inc.
Maxwell House, Fairview Park, Elmsford, New York 10523

Pergamon Press Canada Ltd
Suite 104, 150 Consumers Road, Willowdale, Ontario M2J 1P9

Pergamon Press (Australia) Pty Ltd
P.O. Box 544, Potts Point, N.S.W. 2011

Pergamon Press GmbH
Hammerweg 6, D-6242 Kronberg,
Federal Republic of Germany

The following illustrations are reproduced by courtesy of Courtaulds Ltd:
Figs. 2.5, 3.1-8, 3.11, 3.13, 3.15, 4.4-8, 4.10-13, 4.17-18, 5.4-6, 6.3-4, 6.9,
7.15-16, 8.1-4, 9.5-11, 10.3, 15.1-9;
also the photographs on pp. 118-25

First published 1970
Second Edition 1974
Third Edition 1980
Reprinted 1983

Phototypeset in V.I.P. Times by
Western Printing Services Ltd, Bristol

Printed in Grest Britain by A. Wheaton & Co. Ltd, Exeter (WPS)

ISBN 0 08 024974 4

Contents

Introduction   vii

1   Introduction to the Basic Chemistry and Concept of Textiles   1

2   Production of the Natural Fibres   6
Fibres of vegetable origin   6
Fibres of animal origin   16
Fibres of mineral origin   25

3   Fibre Manufacture   26
Spinning   26
Viscose   30
Acetates   36
Synthetic polymers   40
Nylons   41
Polyesters   44
Acrylics   48
Shorter notes on the less significant fibres, in terms
of quantities produced   51

4   Yarn Manufacture   56
Traditional spinning methods   56
Open-end spinning   63
Tow-to-top conversion   65
Count and twist   68
Bulked and textured yarns   70
Speciality yarns   76

5   Preparation of Yarn for Fabric Manufacture   80
Packaging or winding   84
Warping   84
Sizing   85
Looming   86

6   Fabric Manufacture: Weaving   89
The conventional loom and the method of weaving   89
The improvement of conventional looms and the development
of new methods of inserting the weft   94
Fabric structures: weaves   99

7   Fabric Manufacture: Knitting   103
The different knitting constructions   103
The basic mechanisms of knitting and the machines used   111

Photographs Illustrating Typical Fabric Types   118

8 Fabrics Produced by Unconventional Methods 126
    Adhesive bonding of fibrous webs 127
    The production, properties and uses of needle-bonded fabrics 128
    The production, properties and uses of stitch-bonded fabrics 130
    Spun-bonded fabrics 134

9 The Processing of Textiles: Conversion of Grey Cloth 136
    Purification and preliminary processing 137
    Coloration 141
    Finishing 152

10 Properties – Fibres, Yarns and Fabrics 157

11 Uses – Suitability for Purpose 173
    Clothing, including fashion articles 173
    Carpets, upholstery and soft furnishings 178
    Household linen, towels and blankets 182
    Industrial uses 184

12 Comfort in Wear 186
    Body and skin temperatures 186
    The 'feel' of fabrics 187
    The 'warmth' of fabrics 187
    The uptake of water vapour 188
    'Sorption' heat of clothing 188
    The uptake of water 188
    The development of static electricity 189

13 Labelling 191
    Care labelling 192
    Information of importance principally at the point of purchase 199

14 The Making-up of Garments 202
    Choice of linings and accessories 202
    Cutting out 203
    Sewing 204

15 Identification of Fibres 206
    The burning test 206
    Microscopic examination 206
    Solubility and swelling 207
    Staining tests 214

Glossary of Textile Terms Used in the Text 217

Trade Marks Used in the Text 225

Index 229

Introduction

THE author appreciates that there are many courses which require a knowledge of textiles at various levels, and for which only a limited number of textbooks are available. In many cases the student is expected to have a general idea of the complete textile story from the raw materials to the fibres, yarns, fabrics and garments, but the amount of detail required on particular parts will vary according to the type of course. For this reason, this particular textbook has been carefully divided into sections, so that the reader is able to select those topics most appropriate to his needs. The more detailed sections can be omitted without impeding the understanding of other parts of the book.

The complete text is a comprehensive cover of textiles at such a level as to be sufficiently detailed for use by college students studying Home Economics, Domestic Science, Housecraft, Institutional Management, etc.

Chapters 1–3 and 8–15 have been especially prepared to provide suitable material for A-level courses in Domestic Science and Home Economics. It is hoped that the chapters on properties, uses and comfort will be particularly useful to all those wishing to learn about the practical aspects of textiles. Previous textbooks have normally listed numerical values of properties and applications in use, but the author has used a new approach and related these facts to the appearance of the fabric and to its performance in wear, as it is felt that this is the type of practical information required, but not normally provided.

Chapters 4–7 cover the conversion of fibres to yarn and yarn to fabric. The A-level student needs only to understand the basic ideas in this section, and to appreciate the differences between various processes. These readers can therefore glance through, or indeed omit, certain more detailed sections.

The college student will, however, find the more detailed sections, on such topics as the bulking of yarns and open-end spinning, of interest. Those studying textile design and similar subjects will find Chapters 2–9 more useful and the book also covers the subject matter required for the elementary courses on garment manufacture.

For this third edition the text has been updated in order to cover recent advances in textile technology. New photographs are included, showing some of the processes in current use in the industry, as well as other fresh illustrative material.

1. Introduction to the Basic Chemistry and Concept of Textiles

FABRICS are made by interweaving threads or yarns, and these yarns, in their turn, are produced by twisting together long, thin fibres. There are two main types of yarn available, continuous-filament yarn and spun yarn, although techniques have been developed for producing yarns by splitting a film.

Continuous filament yarns are made by extruding long, unbroken threads and inserting a certain amount of twist to hold them together. In the natural fibre silk, these threads may be a kilometre or more in length. Synthetic fibres are produced as continuous filaments by extruding the fibre-forming substances, in liquid form, through the fine holes of a spinneret. The jets of liquid are hardened and can then be stretched and twisted together to form a yarn. The number of filaments in the yarn will be equal to the number of holes in the spinneret. Continuous filament yarns are used to weave smooth fabrics such as satins and taffetas. By the different processes of bulking, these continuous filament yarns can be given properties more similar to those of spun yarns. These changed properties are developed by the introduction of crimps, loops or crinkles into the straight filaments.

Spun yarn is produced from staple fibre. Staple fibres are much shorter in length than continuous filaments, normally varying between one centimetre and several centimetres in length. Most natural fibres occur in staple form. In the production of man-made fibres, the filaments coming from the spinneret may be collected together into a thick rope or tow, and this is then cut up into short lengths to form staple fibre. The staple length can be controlled by the manufacturer, who can cut the filaments into the length he requires. However, with natural fibres the staple length of a given crop can vary considerably and a mass of cotton will be made up of fibres of different lengths. The short lengths of staple, whether of natural or man-made fibre, are attenuated and spun into a yarn. These yarns, which consist of short fibres held together by twist, are called spun yarns. They usually have a fuller handle than the smooth, continuous filament yarns, because the short fibres lie at varying angles to the long axis of the yarn, and a spun fibre will be much rougher due to the fibre-ends sticking out from the surface.

Many properties are specific to certain fibre types, but one property is common to all fibres: they are very long in relation to their breadth. The most important characteristic of a fibre is thus its shape, and wool and cotton both have lengths more than 100 times greater than the diameter of the fibre. Similarly, a high length:breadth ratio is a characteristic of man-made fibres, and it is this property that enables the fibres to be twisted together to form a yarn. To be suitable as a textile, a fibre must be strong but still flexible. Strength is needed to give the final fabric adequate performance in wear, although this is closely related to the ability of the yarn to stretch, as explained in Chapter 10. The flexibility gives characteristic draping qualities to a fabric.

Fibres are made up of large molecules, which are similar in shape to the fibres themselves. The molecules of natural fibres are long and narrow, such as the long cellulose molecules of cotton and the protein molecules of wool. The synthetic fibres are produced by adding together many smaller molecules to give a large molecule, a process known as polymerization. The material produced will consist of large molecules of higher molecular weight referred to as a polymer, and if the material is to be used as a textile the molecules must be long and narrow.

Much work has been carried out to discover the way in which the molecules are arranged in a fibre. Results suggest that in the natural fibres the long molecules are arranged roughly parallel to the long fibre axis. The parallelization of the molecules is by no means perfect but varies from one type of fibre to another. Where the molecules are well organized and lie side by side along the length of the fibre, the fibre is said to be well orientated. In contrast some of the molecules may be at an angle to the fibre axis. The molecules in cotton are arranged spirally along the fibre axis, but this is a characteristic of natural fibres and this type of arrangement is not present in man-made fibres. The molecular orientation of a fibre is a measurement of the alignment of the molecules relative to the fibre axis. Fibre molecules must be of such a shape that they can pack together; they must be long and flexible without any large side chains.

The orientation of the molecules in a man-made fibre can be controlled, and can be increased by stretching. When nylon is stretched or cold-drawn, the molecules are arranged so that they are more parallel to the fibre axis than they were previously. In a fibre there will be areas where the molecules have been unable to arrange themselves in an orientated way, and these will be amorphous regions. However, where the molecules are arranged in a regular way, there will be crystalline areas. Fibres are thus made up of a combination of amorphous regions and crystalline regions, but a single long molecule may pass from a crystalline region, through an amorphous region and into another crystalline area. This structure is illustrated in Fig. 3.2.

Textiles from Film

Much work has been carried out recently on the production of textiles from film, in contrast to the more conventional method of producing man-made fibres by extruding a viscous liquid through a spinneret, and solidifying the continuous threads. A film is formed by extruding a viscous liquid through a long slit and not the conventional type of spinneret. This film can be transformed into a usable textile by many different processes: one example is the method by which a wide film of polyolefin is extruded and then split into narrow tapes from a few millimetres to a few centimetres wide. These tapes are stretched in a hot oven and wound on to suitable packages. The process can thus be divided into four main parts, i.e. film manufacture, splitting, stretching and winding.

Commercial applications have included such products as twine, ropes and woven industrial fabrics, particularly sackings. One of the markets into which stretched polypropylene tape is penetrating is that of carpet backings. Research and development are showing that a wide range of products can be produced from film, including filamentous yarn, staple fibre and non-woven fabrics.

Several firms are now producing polypropylene film tape. The flat sheet or tape is split-processed and can then be twisted in such a way as to produce a textile yarn.

Yarn Dimensions

Tex   The current system of measuring the fineness of yarns is the tex system. Tex is the weight in grams of a kilometre, i.e.

Tex   = grams per kilometre
Decitex = grams per 10 kilometres.

Denier   This system has now largely been replaced by the tex system. Denier is defined as the weight in grams of a length of 9000 m of the yarn (or filament). Thus, if 9000 m of a particular yarn weigh 45 g, then that yarn is 45 denier. Similarly, if 9000 m of a single filament weigh 5 g, then the filament is 5 denier. The reader will have heard this method of measurement used in stockings, often made in 15, 20 or 30 denier nylon.

Cotton Count   Cotton yarns used to be measured in cotton counts, and this is defined as the number of hanks, of 840 yd each, which weigh 1 lb.

This book deals first with the natural fibres, cotton, wool, silk, etc., and then with the man-made fibres. There are 20–25 different types of man-made fibres and the more important groups are given in Table 1.1. These generic groups are based on the chemical composition of the fibre, all fibres within a given generic group having a similar basic composition. The groups include acetates, acrylics, chlorofibres, elastofibres, nylons, olefins, polyesters and viscose. The manufacturer markets his fibres under certain trade marks; for example, Bri-Nylon, Celon, Enkalon and Perlon are all trade marks for nylon fibres. This may complicate things for the consumer, because of the introduction of so many names, but has the advantage that a well-known trade mark will be backed by the manufacturer, who will carefully guard its use and endeavour to ensure that it does not become associated with inferior merchandise.

It must be appreciated that the line of demarcation between the natural and man-made fibres is becoming less clearly defined, due to the chemical and physical treatments given to the natural fibres. Initially the man-made fibres were developed, and offered for sale at an acceptable price, to supplement the natural fibres already available. They had their own merits, which were, in some cases, different from those of the natural fibres. They were not, and indeed still are not, intended to be imitations of the natural fibres. The future of the textile industry depends on the use and development of all fibres, whether natural or man-made, to provide the widest possible range of fabrics for the consumer.

Since 1930, the world production of fibres of all types has increased dramatically, each of the different fibres, cotton, wool, viscose, acetate and the synthetics, showing some increase over this period. Table 1.2 gives the statistics of world fibre production and the growth of the man-made fibres is, of course, the most striking feature.

Dr Eric Kann pointed out, in his paper to the Second World Congress of

Man-made Fibres, that 'Man-made fibres have undoubtedly made an enormous contribution to improving the standard of life of millions of men and women, to reducing the burden of household drudgery, and to creating new articles of clothing which meet the needs and tastes of our times. What the consumer wants

TABLE 1.1   A TABLE OF TEXTILE FIBRES
A. THE NATURAL FIBRES
(Listed according to origin of fibre)

Fibre origin	Fibre name
Fibres of vegetable origin:	
Seed fibres	Cotton
Stem or bast fibres	Flax, hemp, jute, kenaf, ramie
Leaf fibres	Abaca, sisal
Fibres of animal origin:	
Wool or hair fibres	Alpaca, camel hair, cashmere, llama, mohair, wool
Insect webs, cocoons, etc.	Silk, tussah silk
Fibres of mineral origin	Asbestos

B. WELL-KNOWN TRADE MARKS OF MAN-MADE FIBRES
(Listed according to generic groups)

Class of fibre/generic group	Trade marks
Acetate	Dicel
Acrylic	Acrilan, Courtelle, Dralon, Orlon
Alginate	Alginate
Chlorofibres	
Polyvinylidene chloride type	Saran, Verel
Polyvinyl chloride type	Leavil, Rhovyl
Elastane	Lycra, Spanzelle, Vyrene
Glass	Fiberglas, Veranne
Metallic	Lurex, Metlon
Modacrylic	Acrilan SEF, Kanekaron, Teklan
Modal – see modified viscose	
Nylon	Antron, Blue C Nylon, Bri-Nylon, Celon, Enkalon, Helion, Lilion, Perlon
Antistatic nylons	Celon Anti-stat, Counterstat, Enka-comfort, Ultron
Modified nylon	Qiana
Polyester	Dacron, Lirelle, Tergal, Terlenka, Terylene, Trevira
Polyethylene	
Polypropylene	Courlene
Viscose	Standard Viscose, Fibro, Floccal
Modified viscose	
High-tenacity filament	Tenaso HSR, Tenaso Super 2A
Modal, high wet modulus fibres	
including polynosics	Vincel, Zantrel Z4, Lenzing 333, Koplon
Crimped	Evlan, Floxan, Sarille
Hollow fibre staple	Viloft
Triacetate	Arnel, Rhonel, Tricel

to buy is clothing which is at once light and warm, easy to wear and care for, and meets the increasing tendency towards informal living.'

Despite the fantastic growth of the man-made fibres, cotton still remains the principal textile fibre, and in fact its consumption almost doubled between 1930 and 1965. All fibres have their own particular advantageous properties suitable for specific end-uses, and have a place in the market.

The different fibres available can be mixed or blended with each other to extend the range of fabrics available. Fabric performances can be obtained that are not possible where only one fibre is used in the fabric. Various colour effects and textures can also be produced by blending fibres. An example of this is in cross-dyeing, where two different fibre types with varying dyeing properties are used in one fabric. The finished material will have a two-tone colour effect due to the different dye uptake of the two fibres.

A mixture fabric is one that is produced either by weaving or knitting from two or more different yarns, for example a woven fabric containing a viscose weft and a nylon warp. A blended yarn is one that is spun from more than one type of fibre, i.e. viscose and wool staple may be mixed together and then spun into a yarn. A blend fabric is one which has been woven or knitted from this type of yarn.

Having discussed the fibres available, subsequent chapters cover yarn production and fabric production. The interesting new developments, such as tow-to-top conversion, open-end spinning and the production of stitch-bonded fabrics, have been covered in an elementary way, and serve to illustrate the great technological advances of the industry.

The remainder of the book is devoted to the more practical side of the subject. The properties of fibres, yarns and fabrics are discussed and related to the way in which they influence the properties of the fabric containing them. The uses of the various fibres and their performance in wear are dealt with, and subsequent sections cover labelling, making-up and the identification of textiles.

TABLE 1.2 SOME STATISTICS OF FIBRE PRODUCTION*
(in thousands of metric tonnes)

| Year | World production | | | | | | | Estimated world population (millions) |
	Rayon and acetate yarn	Rayon and acetate staple	Synthetic yarn	Synthetic staple	Total man-made	Raw cotton	Raw wool	
1900	1				1	3 162	730	1 550
1930	205	3			208	5 928†	1 002†	2 000
1935	425	65			490	6 055	980	
1940	542	585	1	4	1 132	6 971	1 134	2 200
1945	401	200	14	3	618	4 667	1 034	
1950	874	738	54	15	1 681	6 647	1 057	2 500
1955	1 042	1 236	184	83	2 545	9 492	1 265	2 700
1960	1 131	1 476	417	285	3 309	10 113	1 463	3 000
1965	1 374	1 965	1 126	926	5 391	11 605	1 493	3 300
1970	1 391	2 040	2 361	2 334	8 126	11 367	1 591	3 632
1975	1 136	1 823	3 763	3 583	10 305	11 809	1 504	n.a.
1977	1 157	2 098	4 315	4 732	12 302	14 138	1 390	n.a.

* Source: Textile Organon and United Nations Library.
† Crop years from 1930.

2. Production of the Natural Fibres

THE natural fibres can be grouped into three main classes according to their origin:

(i) Vegetable fibres.
(ii) Animal fibres.
(iii) Mineral fibres.

The vegetable fibres include cotton, flax, jute, hemp and other fibres produced from polymers made by plants. These consist of cellulose – the structural material which gives strength to the plant.

The animal fibres on the other hand are based on proteins – the complex chemicals used in the animal body. They include wool, from animal hairs, and silk, used by the silkworm in making its cocoon.

The third group, the mineral fibres, are of smaller significance but are used in specialized materials, like asbestos, to produce fire-resistant fabrics.

FIBRES OF VEGETABLE ORIGIN

Cellulose is a chemical substance related to starches and sugars and is a carbohydrate. It is made by the plant from water and carbon dioxide by the chemical process of photosynthesis, which requires the presence of energy from sunlight as an initiator for the reaction.

$$\text{Energy} + 6H_2O + 6CO_2 \rightarrow C_6H_{12}O_6 + 6O_2$$

The formula of cellulose indicates that it consists of many glucose units joined together to give a polymer molecule (Fig. 2.1) which has the required shape for the production of a textile fibre. It is long in relation to its breadth and the polymer molecules are able to pack together.

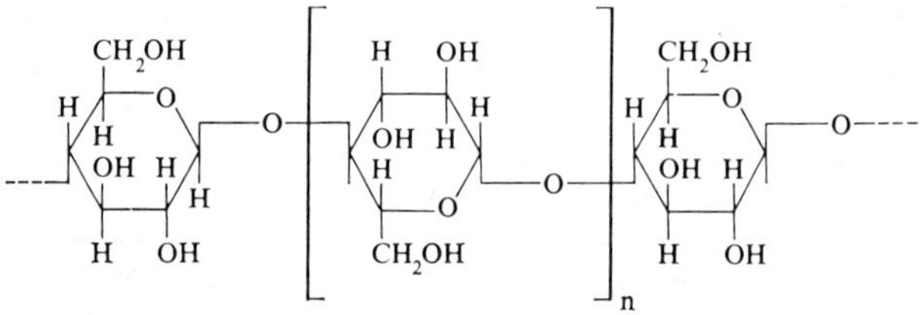

Fig. 2.1   Molecule of Cellulose

The strands of cellulose fibre in plants are associated with other natural materials such as lignin, waxes, gums and pectin. It is therefore essential that the cellulose can be separated from these substances fairly easily if it is to be useful as a source for the raw material from which a textile material can be made.

Seed Fibres

Cotton

The most important fibre in this group is cotton, which is attached to the seeds of certain plants of the genus *Gossypium*. Its primary function is to aid germination, probably by accumulating moisture, and thus ensure the propagation of the species. Man, however, can collect this fibre and put it to his own use in making textile fibres.

History The concept of producing textile fibres from these seed-hairs was known to the ancient Egyptians and by the earliest Chinese civilizations. There is some evidence that cotton was used in Egypt as early as 12 000 B.C. but there is no doubt that India developed cotton production as an industry, fine fabric being produced as early as 1500 B.C.

At a later date, cotton-growing and manufacture spread to the Mediterranean, and in the tenth century A.D. some of the finest fabrics were made in Spain. Cotton became one of the most important articles carried on the great trade routes and the industry developed in France, Italy and Portugal.

However, when the Turks conquered Syria and Egypt the overland routes were closed and trade with India virtually ceased. For this reason the great sea voyages of Vasco da Gama and other explorers took place, in the fifteenth century, to search for a new route to the East. For some time after this, Portugal monopolized the sea trade between Europe and the East, but after the Armada the trade routes from Europe to India were opened and the great trading companies began to emerge.

The British East India Company was formed in 1600 and was followed by the development of Dutch and French companies. During the seventeenth century the industry developed in Britain until she eventually began to lead the world in the production of cotton fabrics.

Acts engineered by the wool merchants, prohibiting the sale of cotton goods in England, were abolished and production methods improved as a result of the inventions of the Industrial Revolution. At this time most of our cotton was imported from the West Indies, with some from India, Brazil and the Levant, but later America developed as a cotton producer. Lancashire was then the centre of cotton-manufacturing in the world, a position which she held until the First World War, when the Eastern countries began to develop their own industries.

The Production of Cotton Most of the world's cotton is now grown as an annual crop and the seed is usually sown in the spring. The young plants develop creamy-white flowers (Fig. 2.2), which turn pink and eventually wither away, leaving the seed pod or boll (Fig. 2.3). Inside the boll the seeds develop with the long hairs attached to them, until they reach maturity. The boll bursts and the cotton emerges as a wad of soft fibres.

Fig. 2.2   The cotton flower (By courtesy of the Textile Council)

Fig. 2.3   The cotton boll (By courtesy of the Textile Council)

Many thousands of fibres, averaging about 30 mm in length, are attached to the seeds in one cotton boll. When they have reached the right stage of maturity the bolls are picked, either by hand or by machine (Fig. 2.4). Since the bolls will not all be at the same stage of development, a field may be covered several times when picked by hand.

After harvesting, the cotton fibres must be separated from the seeds, and this is done by large machines known as gins. The process also helps to remove much unwanted impurity, such as leaf and twig, which is present, particularly if picking has been done mechanically.

Ginning machines are of two types: the saw gin, in which the teeth of rotating saws pass through a metal grating and seize the fibres, pulling them through the

Fig. 2.4   Mechanical cotton picker. This shows cotton being harvested in the U.S.A. (By courtesy of the Textile Council)

H.O.T.—B

grating slits which are too narrow to allow passage of the other larger matter; and the roller gin, often used for longer type cottons, consisting of a roller covered with leather to which the fibres cling. As the roller revolves a knife set close to its surface scrapes away and removes the seed and large impurities.

The cotton fibres are then pressed into bales, weighing about 225 kg each.

The cotton has to be graded ready for sale, and this assessment is made by skilled inspectors who consider the staple length, colour and the amount of impurity.

The quality will vary greatly according to the variety of plant from which the fibre is obtained and the growing conditions in the area in which it is produced. There will be a range of fibre lengths in a given bale, with variations about an average length.

There are essentially three basic groups of commercial cotton:

(i) Fibres with a staple length of between 30 and 65 mm. These are the top-quality longer staple cottons and well-known types such as Egyptian and Sea Island are included in this group.

(i) Fibres with a staple length of between 20 and 30 mm. These form the bulk of the cotton and are of medium length; including American upland cotton.

(iii) Fibres with a staple length of less than 20 mm form the coarse, lower grade cotton which includes much of the Asiatic and Indian fibre.

The Processing of Cotton in the Spinning Mill   When the cotton arrives at the mill, the first task is to break up the bales and remove residual foreign matter such as particles of seed, leaf, dust and twig. This is done by the bale-breaker, where spiked rollers revolving at a high speed loosen the fibres and remove the heavier impurities. At this point various grades can be blended by mixing layers from different bales.

The cotton then passes to a series of machines, which continue to loosen and clean the material by means of fans and beaters, and finally emerges in the form of continuous soft fleecy sheets known as laps. They are like huge rolls of cotton wool.

The subsequent stages of spinning have developed into highly automated processes, with the evolution from simple hand equipment to highly mechanized textile machinery; the different processes are summarized here, but are dealt with in greater detail in Chapter 4, 'Yarn Manufacture'.

(a) Carding   Carding engines open out the laps into a filmy web, to permit the removal of immature or short fibres and impurities, before collecting the fibres into a soft rope-like form, known as a sliver.

(b) Drawing   In order to reduce the irregularity found in individual slivers they are combined in groups of from four to eight for their passage through the draw-frames. The purpose of these machines is to align the fibres more closely and to draw out, or attenuate, the slivers, thus reducing them in thickness.

The production of high-quality yarns requires an additional process at this point, i.e. combing. The draw-frame sliver is made into a narrow lap, which is combed to remove a percentage of shorter fibres which may otherwise project from the surface of the finished yarn. The combed lap is re-formed into a sliver.

Draw-frame and combed slivers are further attentuated to produce fine roving, and the insertion of some twist is necessary to hold the fibres together. The greater the number of drawing processes the finer the yarn will be.

The Structure of the Cotton Fibre Cotton is characterized by the variation in shape of the fibres, each one consisting of a single cell in the form of a tube of cellulose which has collapsed, flattened and twisted as it dried.

The wall of the fibre varies in thickness, but is made up of two main sections: the primary wall as an outer layer and the secondary wall as the inner layer. In the centre is a space known as the lumen.

The primary wall is tough and contains other substances such as wax and protein as well as cellulose. It acts as a protective layer.

The secondary wall makes up the bulk of the fibre and is laid in growth-rings during the second stage of growth. This inner wall is almost pure cellulose and is arranged in fibrils, which are packed alongside one another, running in spirals.

When the cotton fibre is alive the centre is filled with liquid nutrients and protoplasm and is thus round in cross-section. However, when the fibre dies the liquid disappears and an almost empty space, known as the lumen, runs lengthways through the fibre (Fig. 2.5).

Chemical Modifications Chemically modified cottons have now appeared on the market in various forms, in which the cellulose of the cotton has been treated to form a chemical derivative of cellulose, giving different types of fibres with altered properties.

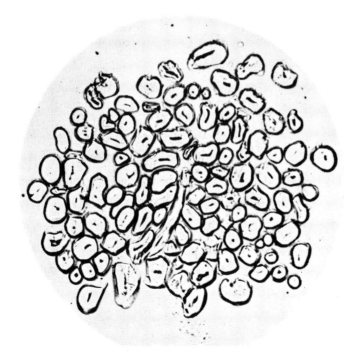

Fig. 2.5(a) Cross-sections of cotton – flat, elongated or kidney-shaped with empty lumen seen as a line parallel to the longer direction (magnification × 300)

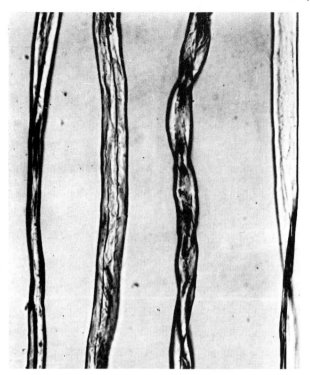

Fig. 2.5(b)   Longitudinal view of cotton – showing the ribbon-like fibres with convolutions (magnification × 300)

One of the most important variations is acetylated cotton, which has a better resistance to degradation by heat and is referred to as PA cotton. The raw material is treated with acetic anhydride in acetic acid. An important application of this material is in laundry-press covers, which must withstand prolonged heating. PA cotton is more resistant to attack by micro-organisms and chemicals.

Treatment with various other chemicals produces derivatives with other advantageous properties such as rot-resistance and improved crease-resistance.

Mercerization   The process of mercerization depends on the fact that cotton fibres will swell readily in a solution of caustic soda. This phenomenon was first discovered in 1844 by John Mercer, who noticed that the swelling caused an overall shrinkage in the cotton fabric, but as a result the material became stronger and dyed more readily.

At a later date it was realized that if the fabric was stretched out during the treatment so that it could not shrink, an attractive lustre developed. The fibres recovered their original circular cross-section as a result of swelling and the cloth had a smoother surface than before.

Mercerized cotton is therefore chemically similar to cotton in that it is still almost pure cellulose, but it has improved dyeing properties and a lustrous appearance.

Stem Fibres

Other fibres of vegetable origin include flax, hemp and jute, which are known as the bast or stem fibres. They form the bundles in the fibrous layer beneath the bark of dicotyledonous plants. The function of these bundles is to hold the plant erect. They are held together by non-cellulosic materials and the fibres are separated from this other tissue in the stem by the process called retting, a natural decomposition.

Flax

Flax is the fibre used to make linen and is thought to be one of the first fibres of plant origin to be used by man in textile production.

Flax fibres come from the annual, *Linum usitatissimum*, which can be grown in many temperate and subtropical regions. Encouraged by the English Government, a thriving linen industry was set up in Ireland. Compared with cotton, development and invention were slow, with the result that linen is now manufactured in a few fairly localized areas, including Northern Ireland.

Production   The flax plant has a single stem with no side branches other than those carrying flowers. The plants are allowed to flower and when the seeds are beginning to ripen, the crop is pulled up by the roots.

The flax fibres then have to be separated from the other tissue in the stem and this is carried out by a fermentation process known as retting. One method commonly used in Ireland to bring about this reaction is to tie the plants into sheaves and immerse them in water in special dams for about ten days. Alternatively the plants may be laid out on the ground for several weeks and thus rely on the dew and rain to bring about the fermentation.

Another method involves removing the seed bolls and then soaking the crops in water in specially heated tanks – in this way the process is speeded up and fermentation is complete within three days. The advantages of this method are the added control over the reaction and the independence from seasonal rainfall.

These methods all depend on biological fermentation but the stems can be retted by treatment with chemicals, though in general this has proved to be more costly.

When the straw is passed through the breaking machine, fluted rollers break up the woody core, and the fragments of straw are beaten with blunt wooden or metal blades, either by hand or by machine. This separates the woody matter or shive, from the flax fibres which are in the form of long fibres adhering together.

The fibres are then combed or 'hackled' by being drawn through sets of pins, each set being finer than the one before. In this way the fibres are separated and arranged in a parallel state. The long fibres, known as line, are wet-spun to produce fine yarns. The shorter fibres, or tow, are recombed and dry-spun into coarser yarns of lower quality.

One of the main features of the flax fibre is the long staple length. Initially a good fibre will average between 450 and 600 mm, but it will normally be somewhat shorter in length by the time it reaches the spinning stage, since the fibres are broken in processing. Flax is made up from bundles of fibre cells, which are held together by the binding material. Although the coarse bundles of fibre in the stem tend to be broken up in processing, the fibre strands are not separated into individual fibre cells.

The fine structure of flax therefore consists of many individual fibre cells and under the microscope the fibre cells can be seen as long tubes. They do not have the convolutions which are characteristic of cotton but there are swellings called 'nodes' along their length, and the fibres have characteristic cross-markings. The width of the fibre varies along its length (Fig. 2.6).

There is a canal running through the centre of the cell, and this lumen, although narrow, is regular in width.

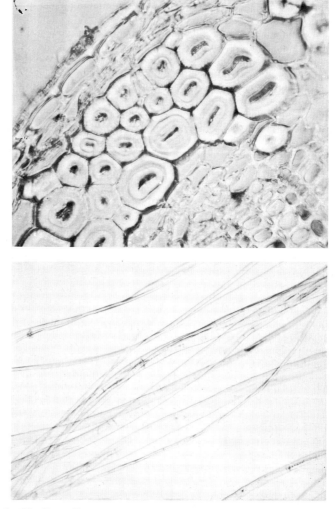

Fig. 2.6   The linen fibre: (a) cross-section of flax fibres as contained in the stem; (b) longitudinal view of flax fibre. (By courtesy of the Linen Industry Research Association)

Flax is a strong fibre and is used when strength and resistance to repeated laundering are required. Linen is used for handkerchiefs, sheets, dress goods, tent and sail cloths and sewing threads.

Jute

Jute, another fibre obtained from the stem of a plant and based on cellulose, comes from the inner bark of plants of the genus *Corchorus*. The plants grow in hot, damp regions, mainly in Pakistan, India and China. Several other countries took up the spinning and weaving of jute, and Dundee is still a centre of the industry, although India and Pakistan have an increasing number of mills for processing their own fibre.

Production After harvesting, the crop is retted in a similar way to flax, the stalks being soaked in water until the fibre can be separated from the stem. The fibre strands, after being washed and hung in the sun to dry, are compressed into bales.

In the spinning mills it is necessary to add small amounts of oil to the fibre when converting it into yarn.

The fine structure of jute is again made up of bundles of individual fibres and these are held together by gummy materials. It normally feels coarse since some of the fibre-ends become detached from the strands, giving the jute a rough handle.

The cell seen in cross-section usually has five or six sides, has thick walls and a wide lumen. Unlike flax the lumen is irregular in jute. However, the cell surface is smooth but has nodes and cross-markings.

Jute is not as durable as flax or hemp and its main use is in the production of inexpensive articles such as wrappings, sacks and bags, and the yarn is often neither blended nor dyed to avoid expense. However, it can be bleached through various stages from pale cream to white and dyed to bright shades. With the increasing use of rugs and carpets there has been a demand for jute yarns for the backing.

Hemp

Hemp is a bast fibre from the plant *Cannabis sativa*, and the plant is grown in most European countries and in many parts of Asia, the most important producer countries being the Soviet Union, Yugoslavia, Romania and Hungary.

After harvesting, the hemp plant is treated in the same way as flax. After retting, the fibre is separated from the woody material and softened by pounding.

Hemp is a coarse fibre and, since it is strong and durable, it is used for making string, rope and cord. Hemp is also used in coarse fabrics such as sacking and canvas but with the exception of Italian hemps, the fibre is usually dark in colour and difficult to bleach.

Other bast fibres include kenaf, urena, ramie and nettle.

Leaf Fibres

The third group of fibres of vegetable origin are produced from the fibres which give shape and strength to the leaves of monocotyledonous plants.

Normally the leaf fibres are somewhat coarser than bast fibres, sisal being a typical example and the most important of the leaf fibres.

Sisal

The sisal plant, *Agave sisalana*, has very large leaves, which are firm and fleshy and develop almost from ground level. After several years the plant develops a flower stalk which grows to a height of about 6 m. After flowering, tiny buds are produced. These fall off and take root in the ground as new plants, and the parent plant dies.

The leaves are removed from the plants after four years' growth and then at intervals until the plant dies. The pulpy material is separated from the fibres by treating the mature, outer leaves in machines which scrape the material. The sisal is then washed and hung in the sun to dry and bleach.

Sisal is strong and consists of individual fibres held together by gums. The fibre is rather stiff and is therefore used for making twine and cordages, although it is not suitable for use in connection with pulleys or wheels as it is too rigid.

Other fibres obtained from vegetable leaves include abaca and henequen.

FIBRES OF ANIMAL ORIGIN

The animal fibres are all based on protein. Proteins are large, complex molecules, built up by the animal body from amino acids, and held together by peptide linkages. They are essential consituents of all living cells and occur in an enormous variety of specific forms. They form the basic constituent of wool and hair fibres produced by animals, and of the silk used by the silkworm to make its cocoon.

A peptide linkage has the formula:

$$\begin{matrix} O & H \\ \| & | \\ -C & -N- \end{matrix}$$

Proteins can thus be represented by the following formula, in which R_1, R_2 and R_3 represent amino acids:

$$
\begin{array}{ccccccc}
R_1 & & & & & & R_3 \\
| & & & & & & | \\
CH & & CO & & NH & & CH \\
\diagdown\diagup & \diagdown\diagup & \diagdown\diagup & \diagdown\diagup & \diagdown\diagup & \diagdown\diagup & \diagdown \\
CO & & NH & & CH & & CO \\
& & & & | & & \\
& & & & R_2 & &
\end{array}
$$

Wool and Hair Fibres

In the textile industry the term wool is usually restricted to the covering of the sheep, and other animal coverings are referred to as hair fibres. When the fibre is obtained from an animal other than sheep it is usual, and preferable, to qualify the term used by the name of the animal, e.g. cashmere wool, horsehair, camel hair.

All the animal hair fibres are based on the protein keratin, but they differ from one another in their characteristics as a result of variations in size and molecular arrangement.

Silk differs from the fibres previously considered since it is produced as a continuous filament, and is the only natural fibre of significance produced in this form. The proteins involved in silk production are also different. The filaments themselves are the protein fibroin and these are mixed with a second protein of similar composition, sericin.

Wool

Animal skins and furs were the clothing of primitive man, but he later realized that the hair could be removed from the sheep, made into yarn and then woven into fabric.

The first domestic sheep in Europe were brought from the Near East by neolithic settlers, who finally reached Britain about 3000 B.C. However, there were wild sheep in Britain long before this, but they were deer-like creatures with very little wool. The woollen industry began to develop in Britain and by the time that Julius Caesar invaded the country in 55 B.C. we were able to spin the wool into yarn and then weave cloth. A guild of weavers was first established in 1080 and the woollen industry began to flourish – in fact the British economy became so dependent upon it that in 1350 Edward III declared that the Lord Chancellor must sit on a woolsack, in order that he would remember the importance of the industry. During the reign of Elizabeth I, woollen goods made up 80 per cent of our exports. Despite the many changes in this country's economy, the woolsack can still be seen.

The Industrial Revolution saw the development of more sophisticated machinery, which was the result of inventions by such great men as Hargreaves, Crompton and Arkwright. This led to a movement of the workers in both the cotton and wool industries from rural areas, where they worked in their houses, to the towns, where they worked in the mills. The local farmers were unable to supply enough wool to keep these mills working and therefore the manufacturers had to buy from elsewhere – Spain and Germany.

Yorkshire became established as the centre of the wool trade during the nineteenth century and eventually the supply could not meet the increased demand for raw wool. Manufacturers then began to recover used wool from rags and old cloth, and were thus able to sell fabrics made from the fibre at lower prices which the poorer classes could afford – with the result that the demand for wool increased even more. Raw materials were imported from Australia, South Africa and New Zealand, and thousands of tons of wool were spun by the Yorkshire mills annually.

These countries, together with the United States, South America and the Soviet Union, produce a substantial part of the world's wool.

Different Types of Wool

The sheep originally selected by men to provide the skins for making wool grew coats containing two types of fibre. The outside of the fleece was made up of long, coarse hairs, which were shed in the spring, but provided an additional protective coating. The sheep also had an undercoat of more delicate, fine hairs which acted as an insulating layer and provided the fibres for wool.

Domestic sheep are now bred as a source of wool; they provide a large amount of fibre suitable as a textile and have only a few coarse hairs as an outer covering. The merino, for example, has almost no outer coat and the fleece is made of very fine wool. Large flocks of merino sheep are bred in Australia, South Africa and South America. The quality of wool is variable and depends not only on the characteristics of the sheep, but also on the environmental conditions. There are therefore likely to be variations between different breeds, and between similar breeds reared in different areas and under different conditions.

Shetland wool has a soft handle although it often contains a high proportion of long hair; it is knitted into characteristic cardigans and stoles that are world-famous. The term Shetland wool is now used to denote an effect produced with a crossbred wool, that is then plain-knitted, scoured and given a milled finish.

These extreme examples can be taken from Australia and Ireland. Wool from Port Philip in Australia is reputed to be some of the finest fibre available, and it is used to make high-quality woollen and worsted fabrics. Irish wool, on the other hand, is very thick and is used for tweeds and woollens. Fabrics made completely from new wool are referred to as 'virgin wool'.

In most countries, regulations govern the use of the description 'wool', and fabrics thus labelled must, in this country, contain at least 90 per cent of wool fibres. A cloth may be described as blended woollen if it contains not less than 50 per cent of wool fibre.

A fabric labelled 'all wool' will not necessarily be made completely from new wool, but might contain some recovered wool.

There is not enough new wool to meet the requirements of the industry and manufacturers therefore break down rags and obtain the fibres from them. Shoddy is the name given to wool recovered from fabrics in which the wool fibres in the yarns are not matted together and they can, therefore, be separated out without too much damage.

Mungo is obtained from felted cloths, in which the fibres are matted together. The separation is therefore a more difficult one and the fibres are more likely to be damaged in the process.

Extract is wool which has been recovered from cotton/wool fabrics, the cotton having been removed by treatment with dilute sulphuric acid.

Recovered wool is of a lower quality since the fibres will be broken and damaged to some extent. It is used in less expensive fabrics, often in blends with new wool.

Slipe or skin wool is obtained from the pelts of slaughtered sheep by treatment with a depilatory such as lime and sodium sulphide.

The Production of Wool   The fleece is usually removed from the sheep once a year, normally as a complete skin, using power-operated clippers. An efficient shearer can deal with two hundred sheep a day, removing a fleece in an average time of $2\frac{1}{2}$ minutes.

The soiled wool around the edges of the fleece is removed, a process known as 'skirting', and the fleeces are graded and sewn into bales weighing 135 kg.

The price of the raw wool depends on its fineness and length, which is expressed as the 'count'. At one time the count was representative of the yarn into which it could be spun, i.e. an 80's wool was capable of being spun into a yarn of 80's count. However, although the traditional numbers are still used they no longer relate directly to the worsted yarn count system. They are merely the basis of an arbitrary scale, on which the finer wools have the higher quality numbers. The average fibre length of the wool also determines the type of fabric in which it will be used. A long wool can have fibres as long as 380 mm; fibres long enough to be combed and made into worsteds have a staple length of 65 mm or more, and short wools, in which the average fibre length is less than 32 mm, are described as 'carding or clothing wools'.

When all the various points of quality have been assessed, the wool is eventually offered for sale either as complete fleeces or separated into sections of shoulders, sides, back, belly, thighs and britch; and again the quality of the wool varies in the different sections of the fleece.

The Processing of Wool   The wool as it arrives at the mill is dirty and contains as much as 50 per cent by weight of impurities such as dust, grease and perspiration and these must be removed before processing. The raw wool is washed with warm detergent solution in large tanks and then squeezed between rollers before passing to the next tank. After three or four scourings it is rinsed in clean water and dried. In some cases the wool is cleaned in a grease solvent such as paraffin instead of the detergent solution. The yield, or weight of clean wool remaining after scouring, varies according to grade and area of production but is normally 50–80 per cent.

Wool may be spun into two types of yarn, woollen and worsted, and the process varies accordingly. The processes are dealt with in greater detail in Chapter 4.

Woollen Yarns

Materials like blankets and tweeds are produced from woollen yarns; wool of shorter fibre length is usually used and only a limited amount of twist is inserted in the yarn during spinning.

Impurities which have not been removed by scouring are destroyed by soaking the wool in hot dilute sulphuric acid or by heating it in the presence of hydrochloric acid gas. This process is known as carbonizing, and the vegetable matter can then be removed mechanically by heavy crushing rollers, which break up the burrs, etc., into a powder, which is extracted during carding. At this stage the wool is often blended, either by mixing various qualities together or by mixing with another fibre.

(a) Carding   As with the raw cotton material it is necessary to separate the entangled fibres. This is done by passing the wool through carding machines, which are made up of large rollers covered with sharp wires; these produce a thin blanket of fibres.

(b) Spinning   This blanket is then divided into ribbons, about 3 cm wide, known as slubbings. The slubbings, in which the fibres lie preferentially in the longitudinal direction, are then drawn out and spun, a small quantity of twist being put into the yarn, which is rather thick and full.

Worsted Yarns

These yarns are often woven into fine suitings and dress materials.

In a worsted yarn the fibres are more organized and lie closely together along the direction of the yarn, which is more highly twisted.

It is these factors of closer alignment and higher degree of twist which give the worsted yarn its typical fine, firm and smooth characteristics. The wool is carded to disentangle the fibres and the resulting sheet of fibres is collected together to form a sliver.

If the wool is made of very long staple, instead of carding, it is often passed through a gilling machine, in which it is combed by rows of pins moving through the fibre mass. The fibres are thus straightened and aligned, so that they lie parallel and in the direction of the length of the material.

This process is continued by passing the wool through combing machines, which, in addition to aligning the longer fibres, also remove the shorter ones.

The combed wool is known as 'top' and it is then drawn out into a roving and spun by inserting twist into the worsted yarn.

The Structure of the Wool Fibre

The skin of the sheep contains numerous follicles. The wool fibre grows through a tiny hole in this organ, and the young fibre tapers to a point at the top. Above the skin level the fibre is dead, composed mainly of the protein keratin, the growing point being at the base of the follicle.

There are three distinct regions to the wool fibre: an outer covering known as the epidermis or cuticle, which has a thin membrane over scale cells; the bulk of the fibre, the cortex; and, at the centre, a hollow core, the medulla.

On the outside of the fibre is a thin, water-repellent membrane, which gives protection and, like a layer of wax, repels water. There are many microscopic pores in this epicuticle through which water vapour may pass, and the wool can thus absorb water vapour from the body. Beneath this thin membrane are the irregular scales, which project towards the tip of the fibre and overlap one another. These scales fit closely together, and the number varies greatly depending on the fineness of the fibre.

The cortex makes up the bulk of the wool fibre, and consists of millions of long, spindle-shaped cells held together by a strong binding material. These cells are built up from fibrils, which are in turn constructed from even smaller units, and these structures lie roughly parallel to the long axis of the spindle cells. This basic arrangement of the material composing the cortex gives the wool fibre its strength and elasticity (Fig. 2.7).

Many wool fibres, particularly the coarser ones, have a hollow space in the centre, known as the medulla. Although sometimes empty, it may contain a loose network of open cell walls, and the size of the medulla varies considerably.

Wool fibres have a characteristic waviness, or crimp, which enables them to hold together when twisted into yarn. This waviness gives a characteristic elasticity to wool fibres, which can be stretched out and then relaxed to the crimped form, rather like a spring.

This physical structure of the fibre explains the reason for the shrinkage and felting of wool which, with other properties, will be discussed in the later chapter on yarn and fabric properties (Chapter 10, p. 166).

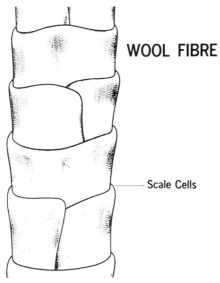

WOOL FIBRE

Scale Cells

Fig. 2.7(a)   Illustration of the structure of the wool fibre, showing scales

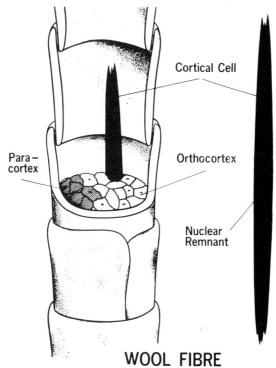

Cortical Cell

Para – cortex

Orthocortex

Nuclear Remnant

WOOL FIBRE

Fig. 2.7(b)   Section of Fig. 2.7(a), showing structure of cortex

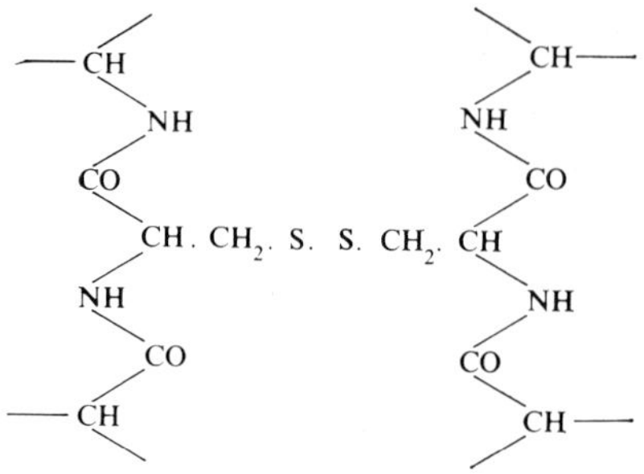

Fig. 2.8   Disulphide linkage

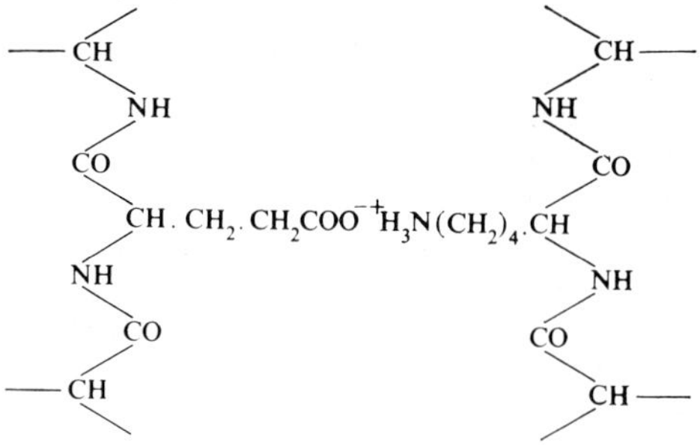

Fig. 2.9   Salt linkage

Wool, like all other proteins, is composed of α-amino acids joined together to form a polypeptide chain. The protein of wool is keratin, and certain of the amino acids, such as cystine, contain sulphur. The long molecules can be held together by linkages between the sulphur-containing acids, known as disulphide linkages (Fig. 2.8).

Salt linkages (Fig. 2.9) can also be formed between the protein chains, by association of free carboxyl and amino groups.

The elasticity of wool is explained by the fact that the molecules are in a folded state and can become straightened when the wool is stretched. Nevertheless, the cross-linkages between the molecules tend to resist any permanent alteration in shape.

When these linkages are broken down, the molecules can move more freely relative to one another, and permanent deformation can take place. The linkages can then be re-formed in new positions.

Other Animal Hair Fibres

Although wool is the most important of the animal hair fibres, there are others used in considerable quantities.

Mohair is obtained from the angora goat and provides a long fibre which produces hard-wearing fabrics, that dye well and have an attractive lustre.

The Tibetan Kashmir goat has an outer coat of long, coarse hair but beneath this is a layer of fine, soft fibres, which are the source of the extremely fine cashmere wool fibres in high-quality garments.

Camel hair is shed by the camel; the locks are collected, the softer inner coat being used as a warm and comfortable textile fibre. The outer, coarse hairs are sometimes made into blankets and ropes.

Other hair fibres include llama, alpaca and the fibres from similar animals.

Silk

Silk is another animal fibre, produced in limited quantities, and noted for its aesthetic appeal and luxurious qualities.

The silkworm spins the silk in order to wrap the fibre round itself as a cocoon. It is inside this cocoon that it changes into a chrysalis.

History China was the first country to develop a silk industry, dating from about 2640 B.C. when an empress first learnt how to make herself a beautiful gown from the fibres of the cocoons. The Japanese then learnt the art, but it was a long time before silk production spread westward. In the first century A.D. silk was one of the treasures from the East, and eventually a supply of eggs was brought to Europe and from these the silkworms were produced, as the basis of an industry in Europe. However, silk cultivation is a more economic proposition in places where cheap labour is available and it is therefore in China, Japan, India and Italy that sericulture has become most important.

The development of the new man-made fibres, such as acetate, triacetate and nylon, has to some extent provided an alternative to silk in many end-uses. Silk has now become a luxury fibre for use in certain specialized fields.

The Production of Silk The silkworm is the larval stage of the moth *Bombyx mori*, and lives and feeds on the leaves of the mulberry tree. The eggs are spread out on trays in a shed and hatched by artificial warming. When the larvae begin to hatch out, a layer of perforated paper is placed over them with a supply of mulberry leaves on it. The worms then climb through the holes and begin feeding on the leaves.

At this stage in its life the silkworm does nothing but feed and then rests for periods during which it sheds its skin and grows a new one. After the fourth moulting, the silkworm has one last really large feed, eating something like twenty times its own weight of leaves and becoming a well-fattened caterpillar full of liquid silk. The silkworm then moves to the straw provided and begins to make a cocoon.

The silk is contained in two glands which have a common exit to the exterior by a small hole in the head of the silkworm, known as the spinneret. As the silk is spun by the silkworm it hardens into two fine threads, one from each gland, stuck together by a gum called sericin. The silkworm gradually wraps itself in this continuous silk strand, which can be over a kilometre in length. In its natural habitat the silkworm changes into a chrysalis and eventually hatches into a moth, which will lay more eggs and begin the life cycle again. In order to get out of the cocoon the moth secretes a substance which dissolves away some of the cocoon, and makes an exit hole. The continuous silk thread is then broken up into numerous short pieces which would be useless as textile material. This must therefore be prevented and the chrysalis is killed before this happens. Most of the silk is obtained from *Bombyx mori*, the cultivated silkworm, but in some countries 'wild' silks are produced, the most important of these being tussah silk.

The tussah silkworm feeds on the leaves of dwarf oak trees and crops are usually produced in the spring and autumn. This silkworm leaves one end of the cocoon open, filling it only with a layer of sericin gum. In order to emerge the moth breaks through the sericin without damaging the silk filament, making it unnecessary to kill the chrysalis.

The Processing of Silk   The fibres previously considered are all produced in short pieces a few centimetres long but, as has already been seen, silk is produced as a length of twin filaments. The processes involved in making a yarn for weaving are therefore completely different from those employed for the staple fibres, when all the short lengths have to be aligned roughly in one direction and then twisted together.

In the case of silk it is necessary to unwind the filaments from the cocoon, and then twist a number of these together, thus producing a yarn of the required thickness.

The cocoons are soaked in hot water to soften the sericin and a revolving brush is used to pick up the end of the filament. The filaments from several cocoons are drawn together through a guide and are given a slight twist to hold them together. This process is known as reeling, and a skilled operator produces an even thread by combining suitable filaments.

The manufacturer thus receives the raw silk as continuous multi-filament threads held together by sericin. Usually two or three of these are twisted together, a process known as throwing, and the yarn may then be woven into fabric.

The gum is often left on the silk during these processes as a protective covering for the fibres, and it must then be removed from the yarn or fabric. Degumming is carried out by boiling with soap and water.

Only about half the silk from a cocoon can be used in filament form: the rest is cut and used to make spun silk.

Weighting   Heavy fabrics produced from pure silk would be very expensive and the density is therefore increased by adding metallic salts such as tin chloride. The degummed silk is steeped in the necessary salt solutions, which are absorbed by the filaments, and heavy fabrics may contain over 50 per cent of absorbed material. Weighted silk fabrics often have an attractive handle, but they are not as strong as pure silk and are more sensitive to deterioration by light and perspiration.

The filaments of silk are made up of the protein fibroin, which has the general protein structure of α-amino acids joined together by peptide linkages. However, the amino acids in fibroin do not contain sulphur, and there are no disulphide bridges as in wool. This variation in chemical structure explains many of the differences in the properties of wool and silk. As has already been explained, the elasticity of wool fibres is thought to be due to the fact that the molecules are in a folded state in the unstretched fibres. These can unfold and straighten when the wool is subjected to a pull. Silk molecules on the other hand are fully extended and they are closely packed together in certain areas to give crystalline regions, which are joined by amorphous regions where the arrangement of the molecules is more random. The fact that the molecules are permanently in the stretched form and highly organized in the crystalline areas explains the fact that silk is a strong fibre but has very little elasticity, since the molecules cannot unfold like wool molecules.

FIBRES OF MINERAL ORIGIN
Asbestos

Asbestos is a naturally occurring rock, made from several different minerals. The unique feature is the fact that the rocks are formed when the minerals crystallize in the form of fibres, instead of in the normal way. Much of the asbestos used today is obtained from Canadian rocks which are crushed in order to extract the fibrous crystals. The purified asbestos fibre is carded and collected as a narrow ribbon or roving. These rovings can then be spun into yarn on conventional machinery.

The important property of asbestos fibre is its resistance to heat and chemical attack. Asbestos can withstand prolonged exposure to heat and is highly resistant to acids, alkalis and most common chemicals. Its main applications are, therefore, in end-uses where these properties are important, as in theatre curtains, fireproof protective clothing, conveyor belts for hot materials and electrical insulations. The asbestos yarn has little strength and this limits its use to the specified fields mentioned above, although it can be woven into tapes and twines.

3. Fibre Manufacture

THE term 'man-made fibres' is now applied to all fibres not of natural growth. They are produced entirely by the chemical treatment of certain raw materials such as petroleum, coal and cellulose pulp from trees. The line of demarcation between the natural and man-made fibres is becoming less clearly defined since cotton, wool and flax are all subjected to chemical and physical treatments in order to convert them into a form acceptable for clothing, household textiles and other applications.

Textiles fibres are required for such widely differing uses in the modern world that no one fibre, however adaptable it may be, can completely fulfil the various requirements for every end-use. The physical character of individual fibres cannot be changed completely, so there is need for a wide selection of fibres, each with its own group of special characteristics. There are 20–25 different types of man-made fibres with individual properties, differing from each other and required either for blending with other yarns or fibres or for certain end-uses for which the fibres are particularly suitable. Sixteen of the most important groups are shown in Table 1.1.

The manufacturing processes for all man-made fibres are in principle the same.

SPINNING

The first stage of fibre production involves the conversion of the fibre-forming material into a viscous liquid. This can be done either by dissolving the material in a solvent, or by heating it until it melts. In this form the long molecules which will produce the fibre are free to move and are more or less randomly arranged.

The liquid is then forced through very small holes in a spinneret so that it emerges as fine jets of liquid (Fig. 3.1).

These threads are hardened, forming a solid rod having the superficial characteristics of a filament such as silk. This extrusion of the viscous liquid through the fine holes in the spinneret, followed by the hardening of the fine jets to form filaments, is described as spinning. Before collecting the yarn it is stretched while still soft and this results in the fibre molecules lying approximately in a direction parallel to one another and the axis of the filament (Fig. 3.2).

In some areas molecules become more closely packed into a regular arrangement and these more organized areas are known as crystalline regions. This gives rise to the picture of a fibre with crystalline areas embedded in amorphous material as illustrated in Fig. 3.2 and explained in Chapter 1.

The hardening of the threads from the spinneret may be carried out in one of several ways:

Wet Spinning The process of extruding a solution of a polymer through a spinneret into a coagulating medium, where the polymer is regenerated.

This method (Fig. 3.3) is used for the production of viscose by the viscose process.

Fig. 3.1   Spinnerets. The principle of man-made fibre production is to force liquid, under pressure, through small holes in a jet to form filaments, which are hardened by various methods

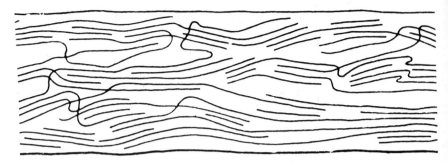

Fig. 3.2   Diagrammatic representation of the molecules in a fibre

Dry Spinning   The process of extruding a solution of a polymer through a spinneret into a heated chamber. The solvent evaporates, leaving the solid filaments (Fig. 3.4).

Acetate and triacetate are both dry-spun. In the case of acetate a solution of cellulose acetate in acetone is extruded into hot air.

Melt Spinning   The process of extruding the melted polymer through a spinneret into air or other gas or liquid, where it is cooled and the filaments solidified (Fig. 3.5).

Nylons and polyesters are produced in this way.

The spinning method is usually dictated by the properties of the polymer, although the method used has little bearing on the properties of the fibre, and hence is not suitable as a method of classification.

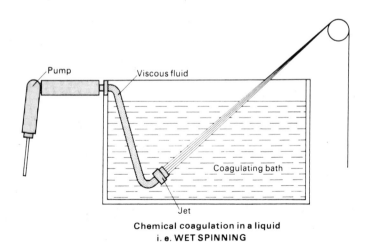

Chemical coagulation in a liquid
i. e. WET SPINNING

Fig. 3.3   Wet spinning

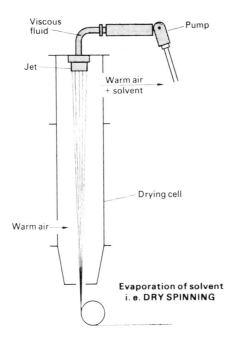

Fig. 3.4   Dry spinning

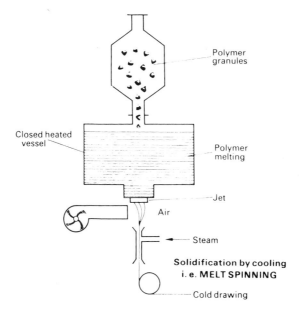

Fig. 3.5   Melt spinning

VISCOSE

History   The generic term viscose is used for regenerated cellulose fibre obtained by the viscose process. In the past the generic term rayon was used for this group of fibres. The regenerated cellulose fibre obtained by the cuprammonium process is referred to as cuprammonium rayon.

In 1664 Robert Hooke, an English scientist, published a book called *Micrographia*, in which he predicted that it should be possible to make fibres in a similar way to the production of silk by the silkworm, simply by forcing a liquid through tiny holes.

However, it was nearly 200 years before Hooke's suggestion was successfully tried out. In 1842 an English weaver, Louis Schwabe, devised a machine for making filaments by forcing liquids through very fine holes. He used glass, which after melting was forced through the holes and cooled to a solid once it came into contact with the atmosphere. At that time glass fibre could not be satisfactorily processed.

In 1855 George Audemars discovered that, on dipping a needle into a solution of nitrocellulose (gun cotton) in a mixture of ether and alcohol, he was able to draw out a filament, which dried and hardened in the air and could be wound up on to a reel. These nitrocellulose fibres were an advancement towards the production of a commercial fibre but the fact that they were so inflammable precluded any great use of the fibres for making textiles.

Sir Joseph Swan in 1883 was looking for a method of making filaments for electric-light bulbs, and patented a process for extruding nitrocellulose solution through fine holes to form filaments, followed by a chemical treatment of the filaments to convert explosively inflammable nitrocellulose into cellulose filaments which could be safely handled and worn. In 1885, Swan exhibited textiles made from this 'artificial silk'.

(a) Chardonnet Silk   Meanwhile, Count Hilaire de Chardonnet began his experiments in France. In 1844 he made his first nitrocellulose fibres. Materials made from these were shown at the Paris Exhibition in 1889 and Chardonnet secured financial backing for the industrial development of this fibre. This was the first man-made fibre to be produced commercially and it marked the beginning of the modern industry, although large-scale production was never realized.

The Chardonnet process is no longer used, since although it had certain advantages, it was a slow, potentially dangerous and expensive operation.

(b) Cuprammonium Process   In 1890 it was discovered that regenerated cellulose filaments could be produced by extruding a solution of cellulose dissolved in cuprammonium liquid into a coagulating bath. The cuprammonium process was developed into a commercially important process and is still in operation today, though not in Britain. It had special qualities which made it suitable for particular outlets.

(c) Viscose Process   In 1892 a process was patented by Cross, Bevan and Beadle: cellulose was converted to cellulose xanthate which could then be dissolved, giving a solution known as viscose. When the viscose was extruded into an acid bath, cellulose was regenerated.

Production of Viscose   The cellulose comes from wood and after purification is treated with caustic soda, which converts it into alkali cellulose. It is then treated with carbon disulphide, which converts it into sodium cellulose xanthate, and

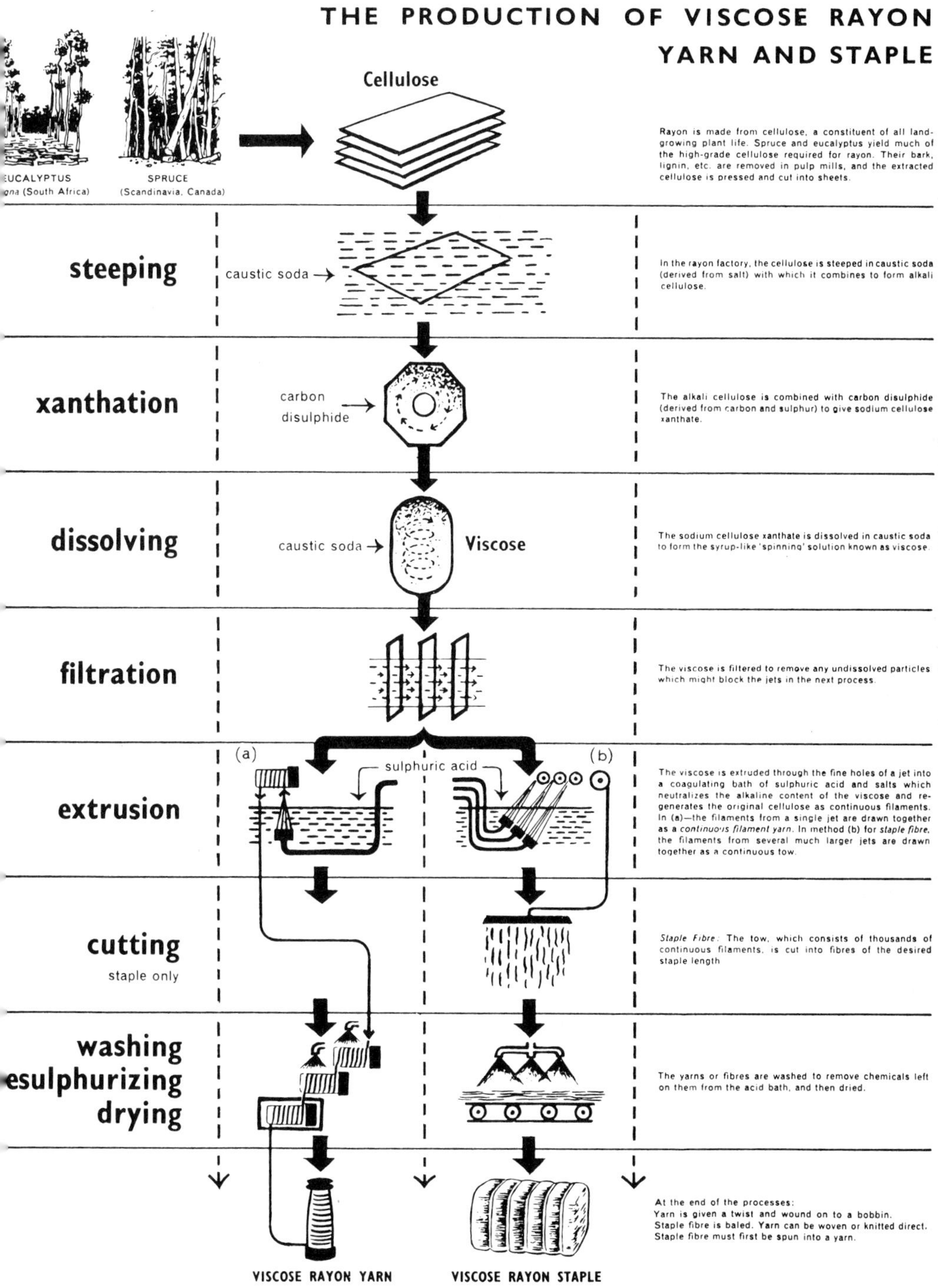

THE PRODUCTION OF VISCOSE RAYON YARN AND STAPLE

Cellulose

EUCALYPTUS
gna (South Africa)

SPRUCE
(Scandinavia, Canada)

Rayon is made from cellulose, a constituent of all land-growing plant life. Spruce and eucalyptus yield much of the high-grade cellulose required for rayon. Their bark, lignin, etc. are removed in pulp mills, and the extracted cellulose is pressed and cut into sheets.

steeping

caustic soda →

In the rayon factory, the cellulose is steeped in caustic soda (derived from salt) with which it combines to form alkali cellulose.

xanthation

carbon disulphide →

The alkali cellulose is combined with carbon disulphide (derived from carbon and sulphur) to give sodium cellulose xanthate.

dissolving

caustic soda →   Viscose

The sodium cellulose xanthate is dissolved in caustic soda to form the syrup-like 'spinning' solution known as viscose.

filtration

The viscose is filtered to remove any undissolved particles which might block the jets in the next process.

extrusion

(a)   sulphuric acid   (b)

The viscose is extruded through the fine holes of a jet into a coagulating bath of sulphuric acid and salts which neutralizes the alkaline content of the viscose and re-generates the original cellulose as continuous filaments. In (a)—the filaments from a single jet are drawn together as a continuous filament yarn. In method (b) for staple fibre, the filaments from several much larger jets are drawn together as a continuous tow.

cutting

staple only

Staple Fibre: The tow, which consists of thousands of continuous filaments, is cut into fibres of the desired staple length.

washing desulphurizing drying

The yarns or fibres are washed to remove chemicals left on them from the acid bath, and then dried.

At the end of the processes:
Yarn is given a twist and wound on to a bobbin.
Staple fibre is baled. Yarn can be woven or knitted direct.
Staple fibre must first be spun into a yarn.

VISCOSE RAYON YARN   VISCOSE RAYON STAPLE

Fig. 3.6   Flow chart of viscose production

dissolved in a dilute solution of caustic soda. This solution, known as viscose, is then ripened and spun into an acid coagulating bath, which precipitates the cellulose in the form of a viscose filament (Fig. 3.6).

The British rights of the viscose process were purchased by Courtaulds in 1904 and they have developed it into the most successful method of viscose manufacture in the world. The manufacture is a comparatively lengthy process and involves many accurately controlled stages. However, the raw materials are cheap and viscose now accounts for some 30 per cent of world man-made fibre production.

(a) Preparation of the Wood Pulp The starting material is timber, usually spruce or eucalyptus. This is cut into chips and treated to purify the cellulose. On treatment with steam a pulp, consisting of 90–94 per cent cellulose, forms and this is supplied either as flat white sheets of board or as flock. On reaching the factory this is stored under controlled conditions of humidity and temperature until the moisture is distributed uniformly. This 'conditioning' may take several weeks.

The original viscose process was a batch process as described below, but on more modern plants certain operations are carried out by continuous processing.

(b) Formation of Soda Cellulose or Alkali Cellulose – Steeping The wood pulp is soaked in caustic soda solution and then pressed to remove the excess solution. This leaves a moist mass of soda cellulose which passes to a shredding machine, where it is broken up into fine crumbs. The crumbs are aged for a day or two and changes take place which greatly influence the properties of the yarn that will eventually be made.

The chemical reaction is usually expressed:

$$(C_6H_{10}O_5)_n + n\,NaOH \rightarrow (C_6H_9O_4ONa)_n + nH_2O$$

cellulose   caustic soda   soda cellulose

(c) Sodium Cellulose Xanthate Production After ageing, the soda cellulose crumbs are churned up together with carbon disulphide in a revolving drum. The crumbs gradually turn orange as the sodium cellulose xanthate is formed and the batch is then tipped into a dilute solution of caustic soda, forming a thick orange-brown solution, known as viscose.

The reaction can be simply represented:

$$(C_6H_9O_4ONa)_n + nCS_2 \longrightarrow \left[SC \begin{array}{c} \diagup SNa \\ \diagdown OC_6H_9O_4 \end{array} \right]_n$$

soda cellulose   carbon disulphide   sodium cellulose xanthate

(d) Ripening The viscose is allowed to stand and ripen for several days at a controlled temperature and is then filtered. Ripening is allowed to continue until the solution has reached a state suitable for spinning. A vacuum is then used to remove bubbles of air or other gases which would interfere with the smooth flow of the solution during spinning.

Fig. 3.7   *Spinning viscose continuous filament, with the dye incorporated into the viscose*

(e) Spinning   After filtering, the ripened viscose is forced through the holes in a spinneret and as they emerge the jets of viscose enter a coagulating bath containing a mixture of acids and salts. In this bath cellulose is regenerated, which is insoluble in the liquid of the bath. Solid filaments of cellulose are formed, washed and collected on a suitable package (Fig. 3.7). For staple production the solid filaments of cellulose are cut and washed.

This reaction may be represented in a simplified form as follows:

$$\begin{array}{cc}
\text{CHOH.CHO.CS.SNa} & \text{CHOHCHOH} \\
\diagup \qquad \diagdown & \diagup \qquad \diagdown \\
\text{—O—CH} \qquad \text{HC—} \;+\; \tfrac{1}{2}\text{H}_2\text{SO}_4 \;\rightarrow\; \text{—O—CH} \qquad \text{HC—} \\
\diagdown \qquad \diagup & \diagdown \qquad \diagup \\
\text{CH———O} & \text{CH—O} \\
| & | \\
\text{CH}_2\text{OH} & \text{CH}_2\text{OH}
\end{array}$$

viscose

$$+\,\text{CS}_2 + \tfrac{1}{2}\text{Na}_2\text{SO}_4$$

sodium cellulose xanthate

(f) Modification of the Filament   The physical structure and form of the viscose filament can be changed in many ways by modifying the spinning process.

Since the cross-sectional shape of a viscose rayon filament is governed by the chemistry of the process, variations in the composition of the coagulating bath result in different cross-sections.

The cross-sectional shape of the filament may also be varied by extruding it through spinneret holes of a suitable shape. Straw filaments are one example of this technique, in which flat filaments are made by using slits instead of circular holes.

Finely dispersed pigments may be mixed with the viscose before spinning, giving spun-dyed filaments with colours unusually fast to light and washing. Other chemicals may also be added at this stage to produce a matt filament.

Certain properties are improved if fibres have a permanent waviness or crimp. This may be done mechanically but it can also be produced chemically during spinning by controlling the coagulation of the filament and producing a fibre with an asymmetrical cross-section (Fig. 3.8).

One side of the filament is thick skinned and almost smooth, and the other is thin skinned and serrated. When the fibres are wet, they swell more on the thin-skinned side and thus tend to curl.

Hollow fibres can be produced by including sodium carbonate in the viscose. This forms a gas when it enters the spinning bath and inflates the fibres.

High-Tenacity Viscose

In all modern viscose rayon production processes the filaments are stretched during the spinning process. This provides an effective way of bringing about the orientation of the cellulose molecules and thus increasing the strength of the viscose.

Much research has been conducted on the spinning of viscose and it is now possible to produce forms with characteristics suited to particular applications. A process was developed in which viscose was spun into a bath containing a high proportion of zinc sulphate and other special additives and then submitted to continuous stretching in a bath of hot water or dilute acid. Under these conditions the coagulation of viscose is slowed down and this allows the filament to be stretched more effectively, giving yarns with greater strength and improved performance.

This process is the basis for the production of the Tenasco continuous filament yarn.

Modal Fibres Including the Polynosics

The Structure of Cellulosic Fibres   Both viscose and cotton are pure cellulose, but their properties differ due to variations in the physical structure.

In cotton the long molecules of cellulose are laid down in a very organized manner, giving a highly orientated structure, with a large proportion of crystalline material, amounting to about two-thirds of the whole. The crystalline areas are arranged in a spiral configuration within the fibre. This organized microfibrillar

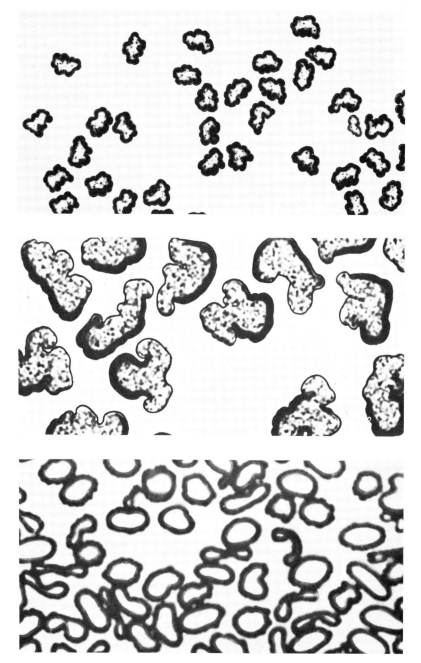

Fig. 3.8   Cross-sections of (a) standard, (b) crimped, stained to show skin, and
(c) hollow fibre viscose

structure of cotton is responsible for its characteristics, including the high tenacity and low extensibility.

In standard viscose the cellulose molecules are much shorter, the structure is less ordered and only about one-third crystalline. The crystallization and viscose formation takes place when the viscose solution enters the acid bath, and the cellulose comes out of solution rapidly. The molecules are thus less able to take up a highly organized state, and crystallization is more local. These fibres thus have a lower tenacity and higher extensibility.

However, it is now possible to modify the method of manufacture in order to produce a viscose which is fibrillar and has a physical structure more similar to that of cotton. This will, therefore, mean that its properties will also be more closely akin to those of cotton.

These high wet modulus viscose fibres are called modal fibres and include the Polynosics. Vincel is an example of one of these fibres.

Production   In order to produce a fibre with a fibrillar structure, it is necessary to reduce the amount of breakdown of cellulose when preparing the viscose and thus retain the long cellulose molecules. It is also important to slow down the rate of regeneration, so that the filaments can be stretched more slowly and in stages, giving an orientated structure.

The first of these requirements is met by carefully controlling the conditions under which the sodium cellulose xanthate is produced. They tend to be milder than those used in the preparation of a standard viscose. The degradation of cellulose is also kept to a minimum by the omission of ageing and ripening stages.

The solution is then spun by extrusion into a bath of very dilute acid, and solid threads of a cellulose derivative are formed. These filaments are stretched in stages to three times their spun length. The orientated solid fibre is then re-treated with strong acid, which regenerates the cellulose. Some regeneration may take place at the first stage, but most of the cellulose is deposited when the stronger acid is used.

By this method the stretching is carried out gradually and the molecules are able to assume a high degree of orientation and crystallization, resulting in the required fibrillar structure.

These fibres are usually produced in staple form (Vincel) and the usual dyes for cellulosic fibres may be used, including direct, vat, azoic, and reactive dyes.

ACETATES

History   Acetate is classified as a cellulose derivative, but its chemical properties are very different from those of cellulose. The Textile Institute definition of viscose as 'a fibre wholly or mainly of regenerated cellulose' therefore specifically excludes acetate.

Cellulose acetate has large groups of atoms attached to the long cellulose molecule at intervals along its length.

Cellulose acetate was first prepared by Schutzenberger in 1869. In 1894 Cross and Bevan discovered a method of obtaining cellulose triacetate and found that this substance was soluble in chloroform. However, it was unsuitable as a solvent, due to its toxicity. At this time the known solvents were not satisfactory in fibre production and the fibres could not be dyed satisfactorily with existing dyes. Hence these set-backs prevented the commercial development of cellulose triacetate as a textile fibre at this stage.

In 1903 it was discovered that if cellulose triacetate is partly hydrolysed back to a stage between diacetate and triacetate it becomes soluble in acetone, which is a far more suitable solvent to use. With the advent of war in 1914, the Dreyfus brothers were invited to England to start a factory at Spondon, Derby, for the manufacture of cellulose acetate solution, or 'dope'. This was used as a varnish for the fabric wings of aircraft and a considerable output was built up.

When the war ended there was no longer any demand for the cellulose acetate coming from the Spondon factory and research work was, therefore, carried out to try and develop a cellulose acetate fibre. By 1921 this fibre was marketed as Celanese.

Acetate differs chemically from cellulose and could not be dyed with the classes of dyes used for cotton and viscose, so that a special one had to be developed. Once this had been achieved, acetate made rapid headway.

Eventually methylene chloride was found to be a satisfactory solvent for triacetate and was by this time available at relatively low cost. Twenty-five years of experience with acetate had enabled the dyeing problems to be overcome and it was apparent that this fibre had some definite advantages over cellulose acetate, for example it could be pleated. Cellulose triacetate fibres have a relatively low moisture uptake and a high melting-point, which means they can be heat-set. Courtaulds Ltd and British Celanese Ltd both announced their triacetates in 1954. They later combined their research work and a single triacetate fibre is now produced under the trade mark Tricel, marketed by British Celanese Ltd.

Production of Acetate Wood pulp is now being used extensively as the raw material in acetate production, although cotton linters have been more important in the past. Cotton linters is the name given to cotton of very short staple length which is removed from the cotton seeds but is unsuitable for spinning.

(a) Pretreatment The cellulose is pretreated with acetic acid. This opens up the structure and makes the polymer more reactive.

(b) Acetylation Acetylation is the name given to the chemical process by which the hydrogen atoms of the hydroxyl groups are replaced by acetyl groups.

Cellulose can be represented as in Fig. 3.9.

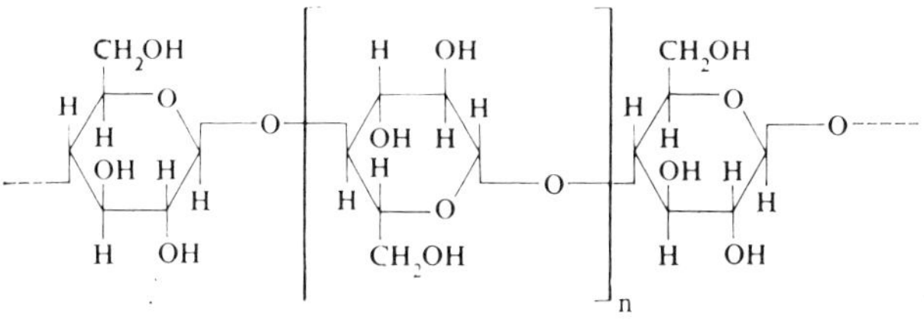

Fig. 3.9 Cellulose diagram

When the cellulose is fully acetylated to give the triacetate, all three hydrogen atoms are replaced by acetyl groups and the formula can be written thus:

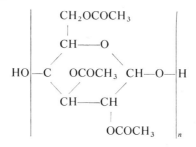

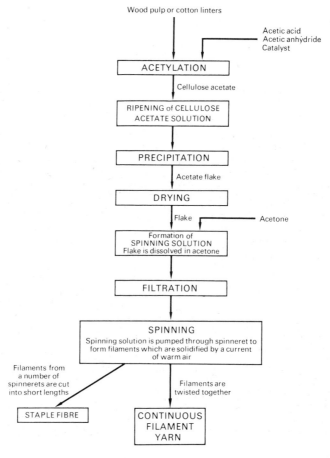

Fig. 3.10   Acetate flow chart

Cellulose acetate is formed by removing some of the acetyl groups until there are, on average, just under $2\frac{1}{2}$ groups per glucose unit, instead of three.

In order to bring about the reaction, the wood cellulose is mixed with an excess of acetic acid and acetic anhydride in the presence of a catalyst such as sulphuric acid. The temperature is raised until the reaction starts; this gives out heat so it is then necessary to cool the mass to avoid undue degradation of the cellulose. The reaction is allowed to continue until acetylation is complete (Fig. 3.10).

In order to convert the cellulose triacetate to cellulose acetate, it is mixed with more acetic acid, run into water and allowed to stand for a prolonged period. Solid cellulose acetate is precipitated by adding water. The precipitate is washed, dried and ground up into white flakes.

(c) Spinning The spinning solution is made by dissolving the cellulose acetate flake in acetone containing a small quantity of water. This solution is filtered and then pumped through a spinneret, when fine jets emerge from the small holes in the spinneret and meet a stream of warm air. This causes the acetone to evaporate and leaves solid filaments of cellulose acetate, which are stretched slightly to align the molecules – thus producing continuous filament yarn (Fig. 3.11).

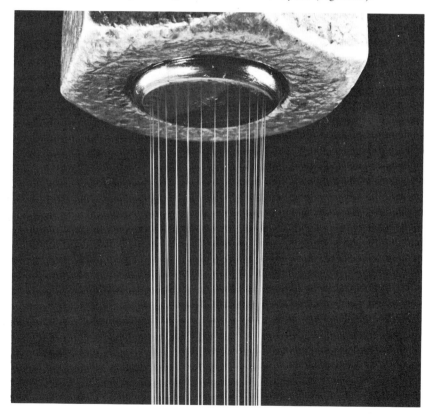

Fig. 3.11   The dry spinning of acetate – by extrusion through a jet assembly. The number of filaments shown in the photograph is 28

(Acetate staple can also be produced by cutting the continuous filaments into short lengths ranging from about 40 to 150 mm.)

Subsequently the yarn may have more twist inserted during a separate operation before it is woven or knitted.

This dry-spinning process is simpler and quicker than the wet-spinning method used for viscose and its greatest advantage lies in the economy of labour. Spinning can be carried out at high speed and there is very little handling of the thread.

Today acetate is dyed mainly with disperse dyes, which will be discussed in greater detail in the sections on dyeing.

The fibre can also be spun-dyed. In this case the coloured pigments are added to the acetate solution before it is spun. They are, therefore, inside the fibre and the colours produced are very fast.

Triacetate

Triacetate fibres are now made in two or three other countries but the method of production is similar to that of Tricel, which is used as an example of a triacetate fibre.

Production of Triacetate   Wood pulp is treated with acetic acid and acetic anhydride in the presence of a catalyst, such as sulphuric acid, as in acetate production. The reaction is continued until all the hydroxyl groups of the cellulose have been replaced. The triacetate is then precipitated into water, washed and dried, to give triacetate flake.

The spinning solution is made by dissolving flake in a solution of methylene chloride containing a small proportion of alcohol. It is then filtered.

Tricel is dry-spun in a similar way to acetate. The solvent evaporates and the solid threads are collected on suitable packages as continuous filament yarn. An antistatic agent and lubricant oil is applied to the yarn and a small amount of twist is given to the yarn before it is wound on to the package. The antistatic finish is very important due to the tendency of cellulose triacetate to collect electrostatic charges.

Staple fibre is produced by the use of jets with a much larger number of holes. The yarn from a number of jets is combined giving a thick rope or tow, which is then cut into staple of the required length.

Tricel can be dyed with most of the dyes used for acetate, but in general higher dyeing temperatures are required.

SYNTHETIC POLYMERS

Nature has provided polymers, such as cellulose, which have long molecules and can pack together alongside one another. By bringing about this orientation, we can change an amorphous mass into a textile fibre.

However, in the 1930s, chemists were working on methods of linking up atoms and groups of atoms in such a way as to create long molecules. This process is known as polymerization, the adding together of many smaller molecules to give a larger molecule – the polymer. Many synthetic polymers were made, some of them being plastics, others rubbers, and it was found that fibres could be spun from these.

Today polymer chemistry is an important part of scientific research, and many classes of polymer are now being spun into textile fibres, one of these being the nylons or polyamides.

Nylon is the generic name for the polyamide fibres, and is used to indicate a group of similar materials all of which have recurring amide groups (-CONH-) as part of the chain. There are several different kinds of nylon on the market, some of the trade marks being Blue C Nylon, Bri-Nylon, Celon, Enkalon and Perlon.

History   Nylon was first produced by Wallace H. Carothers, a brilliant organic chemist employed by an enormous American chemical company, E. I. du Pont de Nemours & Co. In the first place the programme that Carothers undertook was one of fundamental research on polymers, without regard for any immediate commercial objective. However, this work led to the discovery not only of nylon itself, but also of neoprene (a synthetic rubber) and of melt spinning. This is an excellent example of the useful results that can emerge from fundamental research.

Two years after he started his work, Carothers directed his research to the possibility of finding any product that might be used as a synthetic fibre. He found promise in polyester polymers, and finally achieved success with the group known as the polyamides.

Carothers reasoned that if one polymerized molecules that can react at both ends, long molecules would result. If the molecules were very long in relation to their other dimensions, then they would exhibit fibre-forming properties.

Carothers began to experiment and, given a free hand and practically unlimited resources by his employers, he set out to make these large molecules. By building up products from molecules that had reactive groups at either end, Carothers prepared some very long molecules. When these were made from glycols and acids, they were called polyesters.

One of Carothers's assistants dipped a glass rod into a still containing one of these polyesters and to his astonishment the molten material which was attached to the rod stretched out into a long filament as he withdrew the rod, and then solidified. To his even greater surprise this filament, even after it was cold, could be stretched by hand to several times its original length and on release did not return to its original length. It must have delighted Carothers to see his reasoning and ideas so convincingly proved, but there was still much work to be done. These polymers were not completely satisfactory because they were not very strong, but Carothers solved the problem by using polyamides instead of polyesters.

Nylons

These polyamides were made by reacting a compound containing two amine groups with another containing two carboxylic acid groups. This resulted in a polymer with repeated amide groups (-CONH-) along the chain – the characteristic of nylon fibres. The materials Carothers used polymerized together with the elimination of water to produce the polymer known as nylon 66.

$$NH_2 (CH_2)_6 NH_2 + HOOC (CH_2)_4 COOH$$

hexamethylene diamine   adipic acid

$$\downarrow$$

$$\ldots OCNH(CH_2)_6 NHCO(CH_2)_4 CONH(CH_2)_6 NHCO(CH_2)_4 CO \ldots$$

nylon 66

The result of this research, therefore, was that strong fibres could be produced; they were different from any other fibres in that they were synthesized by man in the laboratory from short, simple molecules. Nylon 66 is now produced in Britain by I.C.I. Fibres Ltd with the trade mark of Bri-Nylon.

Another form of nylon can now be made by polymerizing caprolactam.

$$CH_2(CH_2)_4CONH \longrightarrow \ldots NH(CH_2)_5CONH(CH_2)_5CONH(CH_2)_5 \ldots$$

Nylon 6

caprolactam

This is nylon 6, and one example is Celon, a product of Courtaulds Ltd.

A simple method has been adopted to distinguish between the different forms of polyamide, all of which are known as nylon. The numbers of carbon atoms in the constituents of the nylon are indicated by appropriate figures, the diamine being considered first.

Hence the original nylon, made from hexamethylene diamine and adipic acid, is nylon 66, since both these compounds contain six carbon atoms.

Another nylon can be made from hexamethylene diamine and sebacic acid.

$$H_2N(CH_2)_6NH_2 \quad + \quad HOOC(CH_2)_8COOH$$

hexamethylene diamine $\downarrow$ sebacic acid

$$\ldots NHCO(CH_2)_8CONH(CH_2)_6NHCO(CH_2)_8CONH \ldots$$

Sebacic acid has ten carbon atoms, hence this is known as nylon 6.10. Rislan, with the following formula, is denoted as nylon 11.

$$\ldots NH(CH_2)_{10}CONH(CH_2)_{10}CONH(CH_2)_{10}CO \ldots$$

When the polyamide is made from a single constituent, e.g. an amino acid, the nature of the polyamide is indicated by a single figure representing the number of carbon atoms in the original constituent.

The product made by polymerizing caprolactam is, therefore, nylon 6, since caprolactam contains six carbon atoms.

Nylon 66

Production   The primary raw materials for making nylon 66 are coal or petroleum, air and water. These are converted to hexamethylene diamine and adipic acid by a series of chemical steps. These short molecules are joined together to give the long-chain molecules.

These two chemicals are mixed together in a stainless-steel vessel and the mixture is heated. The molecules link up alternately until the polymer produced is sufficiently long to have fibre-forming characteristics. The hot molten nylon is then squirted from a slit in the base of the steel vessel and a ribbon of treacly liquid falls on to a slow-moving wheel which is water-cooled. The nylon immediately solidifies to form a hard ribbon which is chopped into tiny pieces. These are known as nylon 'chips' and are used for spinning.

(a) Melt Spinning A molten mass of nylon is produced by heating the chips and this is then forced through holes in a spinneret. As the threads of molten material leave the jets, they are cooled and solidified by contact with a stream of cold air, and form solid filaments. The filaments are then twisted together to form a yarn (Fig. 3.12).

(b) Drawing In this form the nylon lacks its inherent lustre and strength because the long molecules have not yet been aligned. The yarn is therefore stretched or 'drawn' by passing it round two rollers, the second of which moves faster than the first. In this way the filaments are drawn to several times their

SPINNING NYLON YARN FROM POLYMER

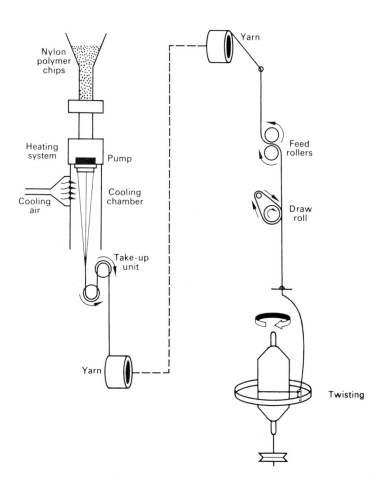

Fig. 3.12 Spinning nylon yarn from polymer

original length. This reduces the thickness of the filaments and causes a change in the appearance of the fibre; it is now lustrous and translucent.

By controlling the drawing of a fibre, the degree of orientation is controlled, and it is on this factor that the physical properties of the fibre depend. Thus it is possible to produce varying grades of nylon. The two commonly produced are 'standard' and 'high tenacity'. In the case of the latter, the drawing is so controlled as to result in a highly organized fibre in which the molecules are more orientated than in standard nylon, and high tenacity nylon will, therefore, have greater strength.

Nylon 6

Production   The starting-point in the production of nylon 6 is benzene, which by a series of chemical reactions is converted to caprolactam. The caprolactam is heated under special conditions and polymerized to give the long thread-like molecules of the polymer. The polymer is melted and extruded, cooled and converted into chips, using a technique similar to that used for nylon 66. It is washed free from unconverted caprolactam and dried in a rotary vacuum drier.

(a) Melt Spinning and Drawing   The polymer chips are heated to form the spinning melt which is then extruded through the fine holes of a spinneret. The filaments are again solidified by means of a stream of cool air, and the continuous filament yarn is taken up and wound on to a package such as a cheese (Fig. 3.13).

As in the case of nylon 66, the yarn needs to be drawn to orientate the molecules and give the filaments strength. From the cheese the yarn is passed over feed rollers and cold-drawn in the same way as with nylon 66. It is then twisted and put on a bobbin.

(b) Dyeing   Many types of dyestuffs, including disperse, acid, direct and vat dyes, can be used for dyeing nylon; these will be discussed in subsequent chapters.

Polyesters – Terylene, Dacron, etc.

Polyesters are polymers made by reaction between smaller molecules, in which the linkage of these molecules occurs through the formation of ester groups (-COO-).

These ester groups are formed by reaction between an acid group and a hydroxyl group.

$$\langle\bigcirc\rangle-COOH \ + \ HOC_2H_5 \ \longrightarrow \ \langle\bigcirc\rangle-COOC_2H_5 \ + \ H_2O$$

benzoic acid   ethyl alcohol   ethyl benzoate

Terylene was invented and developed in Britain by J. R. Whinfield and J. T. Dickson of the Calico Printers Association. This was a development of the work begun on polyesters by Carothers. However, whereas Carothers found the polyamides more suitable than the polyesters for making fibres, the Calico Printers Association made new polyesters with improved properties. A plant for the manufacture of Terylene was built in Britain by I.C.I. The du

Fig. 3.13   Production of nylon yarn. The nylon yarn is drawn (or stretched) by the godet (large metal wheels) and then twisted as it is wound on to the package at the bottom of the picture

Pont Company in America purchased the patent rights for the Calico Printers Association and in 1953 opened a plant for producing a polyester fibre, which they called Dacron.

Terylene and Dacron are based on the same polymer; the fibre and yarn made by I.C.I. Fibres Ltd is called Terylene, while that made by du Pont is called Dacron. In this section, information is given on Terylene, and may be regarded as typical of both fibres.

As in the case of nylon, Terylene is a material built by the chemist from simpler, smaller molecules. These are polymerized to give long molecular chains, which can pack tightly together alongside one another in the fibre.

Production Although Terylene is chemically different from nylon, it is produced by similar manufacturing techniques (Fig. 3.14).

The principle can be seen from the reaction between ethylene glycol and terephthalic acid to give a plastic material of high melting-point.

$$n\ HOOC\!-\!\langle\ \rangle\!-\!COOH\quad+\quad n\ HO(CH_2)_2\ OH$$

terephthalic acid   ethylene glycol

$$HO\Big[-OC\!-\!\langle\ \rangle\!-\!COO(CH_2)_2O-\Big]_n H\ +\ (2n-1)\ H_2O$$

In fact this is the formula for Dacron.

Terylene is made by polymerizing the dimethyl ester of terephthalic acid with ethylene glycol and the complete reaction can be expressed:

$$n\ CH_3OOC\!-\!\langle\ \rangle\!-\!COOCH_3\quad+\quad n\ HO(CH_2)_2OH$$

$$CH_3O\Big[-OC\!-\!\langle\ \rangle\!-\!COO(CH_2)_2O-\Big]_n H\ +\ (2n-1)\ CH_3OH$$

The two products are essentially the same, the only difference being that one end group may be different.

The raw material is oil, which is used to make the terephthalic acid or its ester and ethylene glycol, by a series of chemical reactions. These are then polymerized *in vacuo* at a high temperature.

The polymer is extruded in the form of a ribbon on to a slow-moving wheel. The ribbon of polymer solidifies on the wheel and is then cut into chips for easy handling and these are dried.

Melt Spinning The fibre is spun from the molten polymer by a similar technique to that used for nylon.

The polymer chips are heated and the molten mass is forced through holes in a spinneret; the individual filaments solidify almost instantaneously and are drawn together and wound on to cylinders as undrawn yarn.

This yarn may then be taken to draw-twist machines, where it is hot-stretched to about five times its original length and one-fifth its original thickness. It can then be supplied to customers who may retwist it before use. It is also common to take yarn from the undrawn cheese and stretch and twist it on one machine. This is an example of draw-texturizing.

POLYESTER FLOW CHART

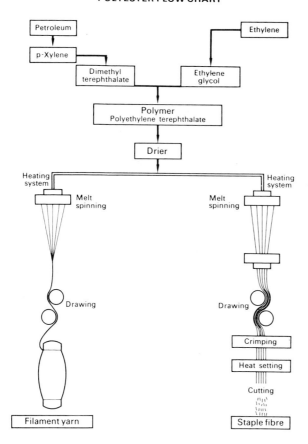

Fig. 3.14 Polyester flow chart

In addition to polyester yarn of normal strength used mainly for clothing, a high-tenacity yarn for industrial use is produced by drawing and stretching to a greater extent, thus bringing about more orientation.

Staple Fibre Production Terylene is also produced as staple. A great number of filaments are spun and collected together in a thick rope – tow. This tow is crimped and is then cut into specified lengths of fibre. The staple length can be adjusted according to the textile process for which it is to be used. A range of fibre variants such as low-pill, high-tenacity and low-modulus polyester staple is now available.

Dyeing Polyesters are highly orientated fibres and the fact that the molecules are tightly packed makes penetration of the dyes difficult. They also differ from nylons in that they do not contain reactive chemical centres to which the dyes may be attached. The only dyes which show appreciable affinity are those which can be applied from aqueous dispersion – the disperse dyes. Azoic dyes and some vat dyes can also be used but this will be discussed in greater detail in the section on dyeing.

Acrylics – Acrilan, Courtelle, Orlon, etc.

The acrylics are fibres based on polyacrylonitrile, a polymer made by reaction between smaller molecules.

All the polyvinyl compounds are made by polymerizing together molecules containing the vinyl group ($CH_2 = CH-$). There are several suitable molecules containing a vinyl group, and the resultant polymer consists of long chains of carbon atoms with different side groups attached.

$$n\,[CH_2 = CHX] \longrightarrow -CH_2-CH-\left[CH_2-CH\right]_n-CH_2-CH-$$
$$ X \quad\quad X \quad\quad X$$

The acrylic fibres are polyvinyl compounds in which the main constituent is acrylonitrile.

$$n\,[CH_2 = CHCN] \longrightarrow -CH_2-CH-\left[CH_2-CH\right]_n-CH_2-CH-$$
$$ CN \quad\quad CN \quad\quad CN$$

The fact that acrylonitrile polymers could be used to produce fibres was realized before the Second World War, but at this time no suitable solvent was known. However, research was carried out in both Germany and the United States, and eventually the solvent dimethyl formamide was discovered. The first polyacrylonitrile fibre to come into commercial production was Orlon, developed by E. I. du Pont de Nemours & Co. in the United States. Others now include Acrilan, Chemstrand Ltd and Courtelle, Courtaulds Ltd and various solvents are used.

The original forms of the fibre have now been modified and new ones developed. Small proportions of other monomers are also added to give a copolymer and improve the properties for textile purposes. This means that the different acrylic fibres vary somewhat in their composition and properties. There are also variants of the same fibre, i.e. different forms of Orlon, but there is a basic similarity between all the fibres in this group.

The generic term 'acrylic' is used to cover a fibre manufactured from a long-chain synthetic polymer composed of at least 85 per cent by weight of acrylonitrile units. This means that the other proportion can be made up of other monomers and the possible variations are great.

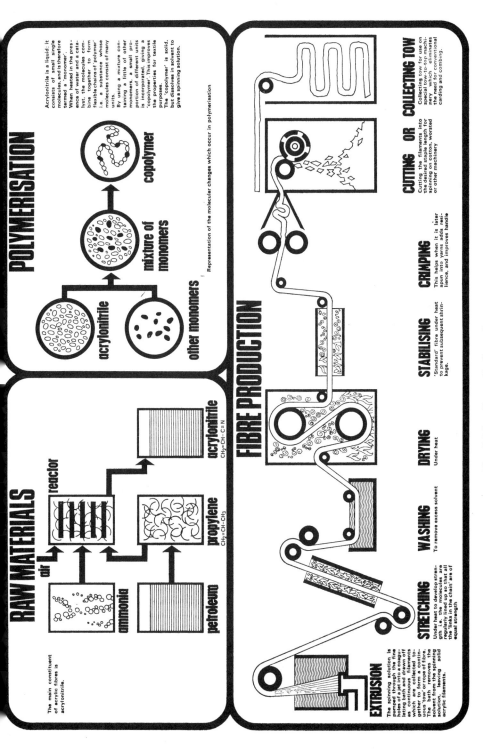

Fig. 3.15 Courtelle flow chart

However, if larger quantities of other monomers are present, the term 'modacrylic' is used. A modacrylic fibre is defined as one formed from a long-chain synthetic polymer composed of less than 85 per cent but at least 50 per cent by weight of acrylonitrile units. This smaller group will be dealt with in a later section.

Production   The method of production varies slightly between the different acrylic fibres and the section that follows is based on Courtelle production (Fig. 3.15).

Acrylonitrile is a liquid and is blended together with the other materials used to give a mixture of the monomers. When heated in the presence of water and a catalyst the molecules combine together to form long, flexible chains. The copolymer is solid and is dissolved in a suitable solvent to give a spinning solution.

Courtelle is wet-spun, the spinning solution being pumped through a spinneret and extruded into a coagulating bath. The solidified filaments are collected together to form a tow. This is then stretched under heat to orientate the molecules and thus develop the strength of the fibre. The material is washed to remove any excess solvent and dried. The tow may be 'stabilized' by heat so that, for the standard fibre, subsequent shrinkage is prevented. This is followed by crimping. The permanent crimp put into the Courtelle adds resilience and gives an improved handle to the finished yarn.

The Courtelle may be sold as tow in this form, with crimp and finish suitable for the various tow-to-top conversion systems. These will be discussed at some length in Chapter 4, but at this stage can be thought of as machines for cutting this tow into staple.

Alternatively, the Courtelle is sold as staple, the tow having been cut into the desired staple length, so that the material can be used on cotton, worsted or other machinery. The staple is produced in both standard matt and bright forms, in varying deniers and staple lengths.

Acrilan, Orlon

Acrilan is manufactured by a similar method and the fibre is wet-spun. However, in the case of Orlon, dry spinning is employed. The copolymer is dissolved in the solvent and the resulting spinning solution is extruded through spinnerets. The solvent is then removed by evaporation.

Acrilan, like Courtelle, is sold as tow and staple, but Orlon is available in filament form in addition to these. The filaments are stretched to align the molecules and twisted together to form the continuous filament yarn.

Dyeing   Like the polyester fibres, the acrylic fibres when first introduced were difficult to dye. However, with the development of modern dyestuffs and techniques, a wide selection of dyes enables a full range of shades to be obtained with good fastness characteristics.

Disperse dyes may be used for pale to medium shades, giving a wide selection of colours with good fastness to light and washing. The basic dyes can be employed for medium to deep shades, and give a good brightness. The premetallized dyes give heavy shades. Although these tend to be rather drab they are sometimes used because they are economic and give exceptionally good light fastness. These different dyes are discussed in more detail in Chapter 9.

SHORTER NOTES ON THE LESS SIGNIFICANT FIBRES, IN TERMS OF QUANTITIES PRODUCED

Alginate

The structural material of common brown seaweed is alginic acid, and not cellulose as in land plants.

Alginic acid can be obtained from the seaweed and treated with caustic soda to form sodium alginate. These molecules are long and can be organized to form fibres. Calcium alginate yarns are now produced by Courtaulds Ltd from seaweed collected off the coasts of Great Britain. The solution of sodium alginate is filtered and extruded through spinnerets into a coagulating bath containing acid and calcium chloride. Solid filaments of calcium alginate are formed.

The unique feature of these yarns is that they are easily dissolved in dilute alkaline solutions, such as hot soapy water or dilute sodium carbonate solution. The uses are thus somewhat limited and rather specialized. Calcium alginate yarn is obviously unsuitable for garments, that would dissolve on washing. However, the yarn can be used to great advantage when one wishes to make use of a material, but then remove it subsequently. In the hosiery trade the welts of socks can be knitted continuously with a few courses of alginate yarn between each. The welts are then separated by dissolving away the alginate. Other applications include medical uses and the production of delicate fabrics. In this case the alginate yarn is used to give strength to the structure and is then dissolved away in the final stages.

Chlorofibres

These fibres are divided into two groups, depending on whether the basic monomer is mainly vinyl chloride or vinylidene chloride, and are characterized by the presence of chlorine atoms in the molecule.

Polyvinyl Chloride Fibres (PVC Fibres)

The fibres in this section are polyvinyl derivatives, like the acrylics, since they are made by polymerizing vinyl compounds which have the general formula $(CH_2 = CH-)$.

The vinyl chloride molecules polymerize as follows:

$$n\,CH_2 = CHCl \longrightarrow -CH_2-CH-\left[CH_2-CH\right]-CH_2-CH-$$
$$\underset{\text{vinyl chloride}}{} \qquad \underset{Cl}{} \quad \left[\underset{Cl}{}\right]_n \quad \underset{Cl}{}$$

vinyl chloride   polyvinyl chloride

Many of the polyvinyl chloride fibres are in fact copolymers, containing a majority percentage by weight of vinyl chloride units. The other monomers are usually vinyl acetate and vinylidene chloride. In the United States the generic term 'vinyon' is used to cover these fibres.

Trade marks include Rhovyl, produced by the French company Société Rhovyl S.A., and Avisco Vinyon H.H. manufactured by the American Viscose Corporation. The end-uses and applications of the PVC fibres are restricted because of their heat sensitivity. The fibres soften at very low temperatures and tend to shrink.

These properties may be used to advantage when producing special-effect fabrics and cloqués. The PVC fibre, such as Rhovyl, shrinks when the finished fabric is boiled in water and produces interesting surface effects. However, care has to be taken in washing and dry-cleaning. Garments can shrink to a fraction of their original size if tumbler-dried at too high a temperature. These fabrics have certain uses in the industrial field, as filter cloths, protective clothing, tarpaulins and wadding, due to their resistance to chemicals and non-flammability.

The development of the PVC fibres has thus been limited to specialized fields of application.

Polyvinylidene Chloride Fibres

The fibres are polymers or copolymers of vinylidene chloride.

$$n\,CH_2 = CCl_2 \longrightarrow -CH_2-\underset{\underset{Cl}{|}}{\overset{\overset{Cl}{|}}{C}}-\left(CH_2-\underset{\underset{Cl}{|}}{\overset{\overset{Cl}{|}}{C}}\right)_n-CH_2-\underset{\underset{Cl}{|}}{\overset{\overset{Cl}{|}}{C}}-$$

vinylidene chloride   polyvinylidene chloride

Saran is a copolymer of vinylidene chloride and vinyl chloride. The molten copolymer is extruded through a spinneret, and the filaments are solidified by cold air, quenched in water, and then stretched to orientate the molecules. Saran does not absorb moisture and is heat sensitive. Thus, like Rhovyl, its application is limited to specialized uses. With such a low moisture absorption it dries very quickly and is resistant to staining. These are advantages when Saran is used to make upholstery fabrics for cars and on public transport. Other uses include filter cloths and insect screens.

Elastanes (Polyurethanes)

Elastanes are of complex chemical structure but are characterized by urethane linkages. A simplified formula is represented below.

$$\ldots O(CH_2)_4OCONH-\underset{}{\bigcirc}-NHCOO(CH_2)_4O\ldots$$

$$CH_3$$

The fibres are made up of copolymers in which long flexible sections of the molecule are joined by urethane links to shorter 'stiff' sections. When the fibres are stretched the folded sections of the molecules can straighten out, but the shorter stiff sections are held together by intermolecular links, which prevent the molecules sliding over one another. Fabrics made from these fibres will, therefore, stretch when a force is applied, but when this is released the molecules will revert to the folded state and their original length. Fabrics have a high degree of stretch and elasticity and can be extended by 500 per cent but will then recover immediately when released.

The fibres are, therefore, used in foundation and support garments and are incorporated in stretch fabrics for ski clothes, sportswear and swim-suits, where rubber threads were used. Fibres such as Lycra and Spanzelle will not perish like natural rubber and they resist perspiration and body lotions, including sun-tan oil.

Glass

The fact that molten glass can be drawn out to form filaments was realized almost as soon as glass itself was known. The first glass filaments were extremely brittle, and this meant that the fabrics made from them could not be folded or bent. This prevented the introduction of glass-fibre textiles on the market at this time and the use of glass filaments was restricted to the decoration of glassware.

More recently, a fibre was produced in America that was far more flexible. By 1936 a process had been developed which led to the introduction of glass-fibre fabrics as a full commercial product with great potential.

The Manufacture of Glass Yarn   Glass is composed of silica and various oxides, such as aluminium oxide and calcium oxide, mixed together in varying proportion for different applications.

The different ingredients are melted together in a furnace at a temperature of about 1370°C, and the molten glass can then be drawn into fibres immediately. Alternatively it can be converted into glass marbles, which are more easily stored and transported. The glass marbles are remelted in a tank or bushing. The glass is extruded through small holes in the base of the bushing, collected and drawn until the filaments are of the required size. The glass is strong but brittle and easily damaged so a binder is applied to the filaments. This material surrounds each filament and acts as a lubricant, preventing damage during processing and weaving.

(a) Weaving and Finishing   Glass needs careful handling at all stages of manufacture, particularly during weaving, when it is subjected to many tensions. Fabric from the loom contains binders, size, etc., and these are removed by heat and by flame treatment.

Industrial fabrics are batch heat-cleaned in an oven, whereas decorative fabrics are given an open-flame treatment. This 'coronizing' process cleans the fabrics but also relaxes the structure and improves the handle and drape. A protective coating for the glass is padded on and cured at a high temperature. A coloured pigment may also be added at this stage. A water-repellent finish is then applied to protect the material.

For the domestic consumer the main uses of glass-fibre fabrics are for curtains and table linen. The industrial uses include laminates, insulating tapes, reinforc-ings for moulded shapes, filtration materials and protective clothing, but these are discussed in Chapter 11.

Metallic Fibres

Metallic fibres are used mainly for decorative purposes in a wide range of fabrics. The different types are made as laminated filaments usually by sandwich-ing a metal sheet between two sheets of plastic, e.g. cellulose acetate–butyrate foil. The sheet is then split into yarns of the desired width. Lurex is one example of this type of laminated product. It is resistant to the usual dry-cleaning solvents, and fabrics can be hand-washed in warm water. Lurex will not tarnish under normal conditions of wear, and is resistant to perspiration.

Modacrylic Fibres

These fibres are produced from copolymers containing 50–85 per cent acrylonitrile. In Teklan, the modacrylic produced by Courtaulds Ltd, the other component is vinylidene chloride. The fibre is made in staple form and has excellent flame-resistant properties. Teklan fabrics in the 100 per cent form are, therefore, being used to produce permanently non-flammable fabrics. When used in suitable blends, fabrics of low flammability are produced. Modacrylic fibres are useful for the production of rugs, pile fabrics, theatre curtains, protective clothing and children's night-dresses.

Polyolefins

The olefins are unsaturated hydrocarbons. This means that there are double bonds between the carbon atoms. The simplest two are ethylene and propylene. These molecules can be polymerized, as shown, to give polymers of polyethylene and polypropylene, which are used to form textile fibres.

$$CH_2 = CH_2 \xrightarrow{\text{polymerization}} \ldots CH_2—(CH_2)_n—CH_2 \ldots$$

ethylene   polyethylene

$$CH_2 = \overset{\overset{\displaystyle CH_3}{|}}{CH} \xrightarrow{\text{polymerization}} \ldots CH_2—\overset{\overset{\displaystyle CH_3}{|}}{CH}—\left(CH_2—\overset{\overset{\displaystyle CH_3}{|}}{CH}\right)_n—CH_2—\overset{\overset{\displaystyle CH_3}{|}}{CH} \ldots$$

propylene   polypropylene

Special catalysts and controlled conditions are necessary to bring about the above reactions and produce a polymer suitable for fibre formation. The polymer is melt-spun and the extruded filaments are then drawn to increase the crystallin-ity. Courlene is an example of a yarn of this type. The fibre is very strong and light, but is not affected by insects, bacteria or sea-water. It has, in fact, excellent resistance to attack by most common chemicals and is thus used in the manufacture of ropes and nets for the fishing industry, ropes for securing loads, agricultural netting, awnings, shop blinds and other similar applications.

Polyolefin fibres have a very low moisture absorption, in addition to their chemical inertness, and this used to present many dyeing problems. However, colours can now be added during the manufacture of the yarn, a process called spin-dyeing, and bright, attractive fabrics are available for deck-chairs, garden furniture and awnings. These can be left out in the rain without being damaged, and the surface water can easily be shaken off before they are used again, due to the low moisture absorption of the fibre.

Polyvinyl Alcohols

Fibres made from polymers or copolymers of vinyl alcohol are very sensitive to moisture and are highly absorbent due to the presence of the hydroxyl groups.

$$\ldots CH_2{-}CH{-}\left(CH_2{-}CH\right)_n{-}CH_2{-}CH \ldots$$
$$\overset{|}{OH} \qquad \overset{|}{OH} \qquad \overset{|}{OH}$$

polyvinyl alcohol

Polyvinyl alcohol fibres are produced in quantity in Japan, where the generic name 'vinylon' is used. Production in other places has been fairly limited, and no such fibre is manufactured commercially in Britain.

Mewlon is the trade mark of one Japanese polyvinyl alcohol fibre. It is light and warm and is used in such garments as baby clothes, pyjamas, underwear, overalls and knitted goods. The moisture absorption is lowered by treatment with formaldehyde, which causes cross-linking between the molecules and thus decreases the penetration of water molecules.

Protein Fibres

Proteins are long molecules, formed by linking together smaller amino acid molecules, and are of suitable dimensions for forming fibres, as illustrated by the natural fibre wool. The protein casein, made by the acid treatment of skimmed milk, can be dissolved in sodium hydroxide solution and left to ripen. The solution can then be extruded through a spinneret into an acid coagulating-bath and regenerated protein fibres are formed. The casein molecules are then cross-linked by treatment with formaldehyde.

No regenerated protein fibre is produced commercially in Britain at the present time, although Fibrolane used to be produced by Courtaulds Ltd. Merinova and Lanital were manufactured in Italy and Belgium. Casein fibres resemble wool and are usually used in mixtures to give softness and warmth. Their low strength and sensitivity to water have, however, restricted their use.

4. Yarn Manufacture

SPINNING involves the process of joining together short or staple fibres by drawing them from the fibrous mass and twisting them together. Spun yarns are produced in this way from the natural fibres such as wool, flax and cotton. Man-made fibres also are produced in this form, after chopping up a tow of continuous threads.

If a mass of 'well-teased' staple fibres is held in the left hand, and a few fibres drawn out and twisted by rolling them between the thumb and forefinger of the right hand, it is found that a number of other fibres become caught up by the twist and can be withdrawn. This process can be extended, drawing out more fibres and then giving a few turns of twist, and a short length of yarn is soon produced.

TRADITIONAL SPINNING METHODS

The fundamental operations of manufacturing yarn by traditional spinning methods are carding, drawing and inserting twist, followed by winding.

Carding is the process of separating the fibres from one another. The material is condensed to form a loose rope of carded material known as a sliver, and this is collected in a can.

During drawing the parallel order of the fibres is improved and the sliver drawn out to form a thinner rope. This is brought about by passing the material through a succession of rollers arranged in pairs, each pair always running at a greater speed than the previous pair.

Irregularities can also be reduced by doubling up. Several ropes or slivers are combined and drawn out to the thickness of one original sliver. The fibres are then more parallel and the rope is more uniform in weight and thickness.

The reduction in weight per unit length of the sliver and the more parallel organization of the fibres result in a product known as a roving. This is reduced by drawing and twist is inserted to form a yarn. The twisting and winding is a continuous operation on modern machinery, the different methods being ring, flyer and cap-spinning. For certain yarns an additional combing process may be inserted after carding. This not only lays the fibres more parallel but also rejects the short fibres.

The Preparatory Stages

The preparatory processes vary according to the raw materials. The natural fibres differ in their natural state and various methods of purification are required before they can be processed.

Cotton   As has already been explained the cotton arrives at the mill in large bales, which, after checking and weighing, are opened up and layers from each are fed into the bale-breaking machine (Fig. 4.1). On modern machinery automatic bale-feeding is possible.

Fig. 4.1   Opening and mixing – layers of cotton from selected bales are fed into the opening and mixing machines where the matted fibres are pulled apart and mixed together. (By courtesy of the Textile Council)

The opening out of the fibres is achieved by spiked lattices or rollers which reduce the material to a soft fluffy mass. Many impurities such as seeds, sand and leaves are extracted. The cotton travels to other machines which continue to loosen the fibres and remove dirt; there are various types of machine but they generally operate by striking the tufts of cotton with revolving beater blades. Around the beaters of the openers are cages or grid bars through which the impurities pass, while the cotton is drawn by air suction against a revolving cage, where it forms a sheet. These sheets or thick webs of fibres are rolled into laps, similar to a huge roll of cotton wool. Alternatively the processed fibre may be fed by air directly, at a controlled rate, to the carding machine for the next process.

Wool   The wool industry is divided into two sections, worsted and woollen, according to the two types of yarn. In general, worsted yarn is combed and woollen yarn is not combed.

The wool hair contains a substantial amount of greasy matter termed yolk, in addition to impurities such as dust and some vegetable matter, and these must be removed before combing and spinning. The material is passed through feed rollers into an opening machine, where the large teeth of the cylinder dash the wool against grids through which the impurities fall.

The vegetable matter can also be removed by chemical destruction by steeping the wool in sulphuric acid. In this process of carbonizing the vegetable material disintegrates and may be removed as a powder by crushing between rollers.

The wool is then washed in a series of troughs. The composition of the cleansing solution varies, but this is often a warm solution of soap and sodium carbonate. The washed wool is rinsed, dried, and then oiled to lubricate it before carding or combing. The oiling also reduces the accumulation of static charge on the fibre.

The woollen branch of the industry depends on noils (the short fibres obtained from the worsted combs), partly on recovered wools (termed shoddy or mungo), and on new wool.

Man-made fibres are processed on modified cotton and woollen systems, though the synthetics will require some different treatments, including less cleaning.

Carding

The aim of the carding process is to disentangle the material completely and remove the last traces of any impurities present. The process also makes possible a thorough mixing of the fibres.

The original method of teasing out the fibres was to use a pair of hand cards, but these were eventually replaced by thick fabric through which bent wire bristles projected, inclined at an angle.

The principle of the carding operation depends on the different actions possible when two pieces of carding-cloth are separated by a mass of fibres. This is illustrated in Fig. 4.2.

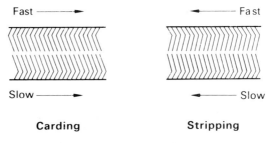

Fast ⟶   ⟵ Fast

Slow ⟶   ⟵ Slow

Carding   **Stripping**

Fig. 4.2   Carding principle

Where the wires are point-to-point and moving in the same direction but at different speeds there is a carding action, and this is used to disentangle the fibres. However, if the points of one set are facing the back edge of the other set, the fibres will be removed by the points from the smooth side, a process known as stripping.

The main part of a carding engine is a large cylinder, about 125 cm in diameter, covered with card-wire. The second surface required for carding is provided by a series of covered rollers or flats. (Flats are strips of card-wire carried by two endless chains over the top of the large cylinder.) The second carding surface moves at a slower speed than the main cylinder with the wires point-to-point and moving in the same direction (Fig. 4.3).

In the case of cotton the lap, or processed fibre from the chute feed, is fed into the carding machine and passes to a 'licker-in'. This is the name given to a small roller covered with teeth which opens the tufts of cotton and feeds them to the main cylinder. At this point the arrangement of teeth is such that the fibres are stripped off the small cylinder on to the larger one.

On the upper part of the main cylinder the fibres are carded by the action between the card-wires of the main cylinder and the flats. Since the teeth are point-to-point the fibres will be attentuated to a finer state of division.

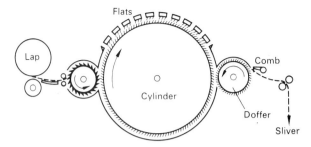

Fig. 4.3   Carding engine for cotton

At the front of the carding engine is another small cylinder also clothed with card-wire. This is known as the doffer, and the wire is set to strip the fibre from the main cylinder on to the doffer. The web of fibres is removed from the doffer by a comb or a roller and the fine web is drawn forward to the centre of the front of the carding machine (Fig. 4.4).

The web is collected into a round sliver or rope of fibres by passing through a tapered hole, and is then coiled into a rotating can. The principles described above apply to the different forms of carding engines, but for wool and worsted the machine is made up of two parts, the first of which is called the scribbler or breaker card and the last, the finisher or condenser card.

Fig. 4.4   A chute-fed carding installation. This shows the stillage hopper and chute-feeding arrangements to high-production cards

Combing

The combing of wool is an essential part of the preparation of worsted yarns, and medium wools are carded first. Cottons, with a fibre length of 4 cm and more are often combed, after carding, to produce finer, lustrous yarns.

Cotton   Cotton is combed if it is to be used for fine, high-quality yarns. The sliver from the carding engine is passed through machines which make small, compact laps suitable for feeding into the comber. The cotton is held firmly while it is combed by pins set in a revolving cylinder. The fibres are therefore aligned and any which are shorter than the required length are removed. The web thus produced is then condensed into a sliver, and several of these are passed together through rollers which draw them out to produce a single sliver.

Wool   The material is combed by needle-like teeth set in a revolving cylinder; the fibres are combed parallel to each other and the shorter ones are removed.

The Noble comb (Fig. 4.5) is one particular type of machine suited to all qualities of wool and is widely used. The oiled slivers are wound into laps and placed below a large horizontal ring or combing circle which is revolving. Inside this large combing circle are two smaller combing circles. The combing takes place on each side of the large circle where it makes contact with the small circles, all revolving in the same direction. The wool is laid over the combing circles at the points of contact and is pressed on to the pins by brushes. As the circles separate the wool is combed through the pins on the two circles. The combed wool remains on the inside of the large circle and the outside of the small circles, and is collected by rollers and gathered into a sliver known as a 'top', from which worsted yarn is produced.

The shorter hairs are known as noils, and remain on the pins of the smaller circles. These are removed by knives at suitable points and collected.

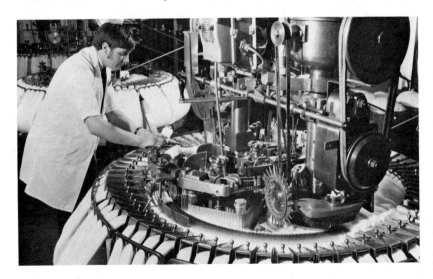

Fig. 4.5   Replacing an end of sliver into a Noble comb

Drawing and Drafting

(The information given in this section refers to cotton and man-made fibres. It has not been possible to describe the variations in processing wool, but the same general principles apply.)

The slivers produced by the carding and combing machines are loose ropes of fibres and the density is irregular since the thickness of the sliver varies along its length. If these were twisted very coarse yarns would be produced with thick and thin places. It is therefore necessary to produce regular slivers and to draw them out. The sliver is then in such a state that fine yarns may be produced by twisting.

The objects of drawing may therefore be summarized as:

(a) the improvement of the parallel order of the fibres,
(b) the improvement of the uniformity of weight per unit length,
(c) sometimes to blend together different materials,
(d) the reduction of weight per unit length, once a regular sliver has been produced.

The machine used to achieve (a), (b) and (c) is known as a draw-frame, shown in Fig. 4.6, and the action is based on the principle of roller-drafting.

Fig. 4.6   The draw-frame. Sliver is fed from eight cans to a single draw-head, where it is drawn out to produce one sliver of uniform weight per linear length

Fig. 4.7   The high-draft speed-frame with travelling overhead cleaning equipment.
Uniform sliver is taken from the cans and converted into a finer and slightly twisted
roving ready for the spinning-machines

The Improvement of the Parallel Order of the Fibres   Roller-drafting depends on
the passage of the sliver between the nips of pairs of rotating rollers. Each pair
runs faster than its predecessor. As an example, if the second pair of rollers is
running at four times the speed of the first pair, then the sliver will be drawn out to
four times its original length.

The Improvement of Uniformity   This is obtained by doubling up. Several
slivers, the usual number being eight, are fed into the draw-frame side by side and
passed between pairs of rollers, up to four pairs being used, each running faster
than its predecessor. The slivers are drawn out to eight times their original length,
and thus the final sliver has the same density as *one* of the original slivers, but it
is more uniform since any irregularities have been neutralized and fibres
lie more parallel.

The drawing operation is repeated to give a draw-frame sliver suitable for
roving. By means of a similar set of rollers to that used in drawing, roving
parallelizes the fibres and reduces the weight per unit length by a factor of about
ten.

The speed-frame, shown in Fig. 4.7, takes finished sliver from the cans and
draws it out. The resultant roving is wound on to bobbins ready for the spinning-
machines.

A stage is soon reached when a small amount of twist must be inserted to hold
the slubbing or roving together, and this twist is inserted by a bobbin and flyer.

Spinning

In the strictest sense spinning is the twisting together of the drawn-out strands
of fibres to form yarns. However, the complete operation of the spinning-frame

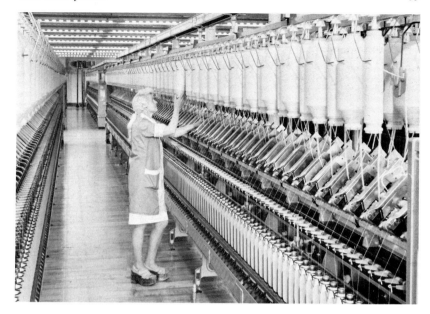

Fig. 4.8   The ring-spinning frame

involves drawing out the roving, inserting the twist, and winding the twisted yarn on to a bobbin.

Ring-spinning is illustrated in Fig. 4.8. The roving from the bobbins at the top of the machine is fed into the spinning-machine. The yarn is drawn out by the rollers and then twisted as it is wound on to the packages in the lower part of the photograph. In order to introduce twist into the yarn the package is rotated. The yarn from the rollers passes through a guide-eye and is twisted as it is wound on to the package which is rotating at high speed.

The ring-frame has advanced a great deal since its introduction and efforts are still being made to improve it and speed up the process of spinning. Many well-developed high-speed frames are available and most of the staple fibre yarns produced today are spun by this method. The maximum speed of production is, however, limited by the fact that in order to introduce each turn of twist into the yarn it is necessary to rotate the package once. Alternative methods are therefore being examined, whereby the twist can be inserted without rotating the package. These new methods are called open-end spinning.

OPEN-END SPINNING

As explained above, most of the staple fibre yarns produced today are spun by the ring-spinning method. However, this has limited speeds of production and has a limited adaptability to automation. It is for this reason that producers have looked for completely new methods of spinning. For some years now there has been growing interest in 'open-end' spinning, where, since the twist is not inserted in the yarn by the rotation of the yarn package, the operation can run at higher speeds and produce packages of any desired size and shape.

When spinning on this system an open end is created in the flow of fibres. Since the yarn being produced has one end free any twist inserted is true rather than false. The essential operation depends on the formation of yarn by separating the single fibres, that are then rotated and joined to the 'open-end' of the twisted yarn, which also rotates. This system eliminates the slowest process in cotton-spinning and production is claimed to be up to five times more rapid than in orthodox spinning, in some cases.

Open-end machines are said to make yarns which compare well with conventionally spun combed cotton yarns. These yarns have some improved properties and therefore less time is lost in rewinding, correcting faults and knotting broken ends together. The packages produced are much bigger and, since sliver can be converted directly to a large package of yarn, many intermediate stages, such as roving, are cut out, and the labour costs involved in the complete operation are greatly reduced.

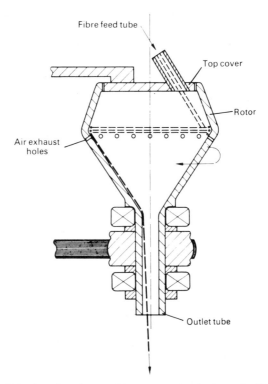

Fig. 4.9   Spinning chamber used in open-end spinning – the fibres are fed into the chamber and guided to its periphery. The fibres are picked off the chamber surface by a length of yarn, scanning the periphery and at the same time twisting around itself. The end is being continually wound off, so forming a continuous yarn

There are several different methods of open-end spinning available. The way in which the fibres are assembled on to the forming yarn varies and so does the means by which the twist is inserted. However, in this book it is only possible to cover the basic principles of a few methods, although it must be appreciated that other promising ways are being developed, all based on the concept of having a break in the system.

In the rotor method the roving stage is omitted and draw-frame sliver is presented to a small rotating tooth-covered roller. This reduces the sliver to a stream of almost individual fibres, which are injected into a small chamber rotating at high speed. A ribbon of fibres is formed at the periphery and held by centrifugal force. As this ribbon is extracted twist is inserted by the rotation of the drum and a yarn is formed (Fig. 4.9).

In other methods, perforated drums or electrostatic forces are used in place of the rotor to assemble the fibres. In the air-vortex method the fibres are sucked into a stationary tube and travel in a helical path. They then join the yarn end, which rotates in the tube and inserts the twist. The point of contact between the fibre path and the yarn path is continuously moving up and down the tube and gives a mixing or doubling effect. The yarn is continuously pulled out of the tube.

TOW-TO-TOP CONVERSION

Man-made staple fibre is produced for spinning on the standard textile spinning machinery. For this purpose the tows of continuous threads from the spinnerets are cut into staple of the required length. In the tow, the fibres are in the form of regular filaments without any entanglement, but when converted into staple fibres these are packed into bales and they become entangled. The spinner then has to card and comb the mass of fibres in order to straighten them out again before a yarn can be produced.

It would obviously be desirable to convert the rope of continuous filaments directly into a sliver of stapled fibres. Machines are now available to do this and the tow is processed directly into the so-called 'combed' tops. The process is, naturally, referred to as tow-to-top conversion.

The tow-to-top machines can be considered in two groups: those that produce the staple by cutting, and those which obtain the staple by stretch-breaking. It is important to be able to control the length of the staple produced and essential that the ends of the fibres in the sliver are staggered. In this way the sliver is held together and drafting can subsequently be carried out satisfactorily. If all the ends of the fibres were at the same point along the length of sliver, obviously it would not hold together and it would be almost impossible to handle the material.

Machines which Cut the Tow

These machines are often known as converters (Fig. 4.10). They are fed with a sheet, made up of several tows, and this is cut by a helical blade. As the blade rotates it is strongly pressed against a smooth cylinder called an anvil. It is possible

Fig. 4.10   Tow-to-top converter

for the helical blade to cut obliquely across the tows; the ends of the fibres are not adjacent across the sheet and this is known as 'bias cutting'. After cutting, the sheet of fibres is fed to a shuffling device, which staggers the cut fibres so as to obtain a sliver which is then collected in a can.

The sequence of operations for this type of converter can be summarized as follows: (1) tensioning, (2) spreading, (3) cutting, (4) shuffling, (5) crimping, (6) collecting.

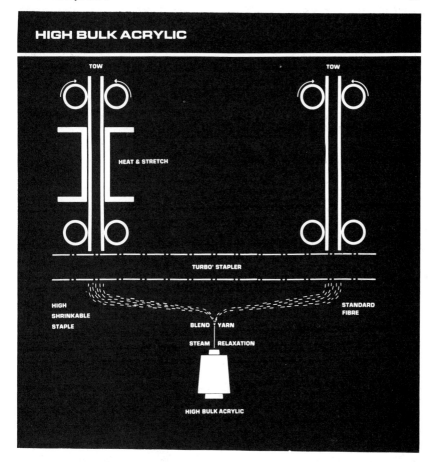

Fig. 4.11   High-bulk acrylic

Another machine, which is versatile but also based on the principle of cutting, is the Pacific converter. This can be used to produce high-bulk yarn.

Some of the material is first passed through a heat-stretching zone, but some material bypasses this area and the final sliver is a mixture of two kinds of staple. That which has been heat-stretched will have a far greater shrinkage potential than the rest. Thus on steaming, relaxation of some of the staple takes place readily and the rest is bulked out. There is, therefore, an overall decrease in length but an increase in bulk.

High-bulk spun yarns can be produced in this way from acrylic yarns and the process is illustrated in Fig. 4.11.

Machines which Break the Tow

These machines break the tow by stretching it, until it gives way at the weaker places. Different tensioning and spreading devices ensure that a regular sheet is fed into the machine. In the pre-stretching zone the material is brought close to its breaking-point and then fed to the breaking zone. Here the stretching is continued until breaking occurs, and the tow is transformed into short pieces of staple.

The material is then usually passed through a crimping-box to give the sliver more cohesion and to aerate it. Often the slivers are steamed to bring about shrinkage, and this can produce high-bulk material.

For the Turbo stapler, a machine of this type, the sequence of operations, may therefore be listed as: (1) tensioning, (2) spreading, (3) stretching, (4) breaking, (5) crimping, (6) collecting.

The sliver will then be processed to produce the spun yarn.

The two processes of cutting and breaking are quite different and therefore the products will vary. For example, the breaking resistance of the material will be increased by the stretch-breaking method, because the material will already have given way at its weakest point. After being cut by the converter the ends are crushed and this makes it more difficult for the fibres to slide over one another during spinning. There are also other variations such as the range of fibre lengths obtained and the manufacturer must, therefore, consider carefully the type of yarn he wishes to make, bearing in mind the materials to be processed, when deciding which method to use.

However, one thing is certain: man-made staple fibres will be processed more and more on these machines, replacing the traditional operations of carding and combing.

COUNT AND TWIST

Yarn Count

Traditional yarn counts and deniers are being replaced by the tex system. The tex value of a yarn is the weight in grams of 1000 m of yarn, so that a larger number indicates a heavier, coarser yarn.

Continuous Filament Yarns

On the tex system continuous filament yarns formerly specified in terms of denier are specified in decitex. The relationship between decitex and denier is given below.

Denier is the weight in grams of 9000 m of yarn
  dtex is the weight in grams of 10 000 m of yarn
  tex is the weight in grams of 1000 m of yarn.

$$\text{Thus dtex} = \frac{\text{denier}}{0.9} = 1.11 \text{ denier.}$$

Staple Yarns

Traditional counts depend upon the spinning system used because a different hank length is employed in each case, e.g.:

1/24s cotton count means that 24 hanks each 840 yd long weigh 1lb
1/24s worsted count means that 24 hanks each 560 yd long weigh 1lb
1/24s woollen count means that 24 hanks each 256 yd long weigh 1lb.

On the tex system the meaning is the same for all yarns.
24 tex means that 1000 m of yarn weigh 24 g.

Yarn Twist

As has already been explained, it is the twist in the yarn which helps the fibres to hang together and the important factor is the angle of twist. This is the angle which the fibres make with the long axis of the yarn.

However, it is more convenient to refer to the twist in turns per centimetre.

As the amount of twist is increased in yarns they become stronger as fibre slippage is lessened, but when maximum strength has been reached, any further twisting tends to weaken the yarn. However, it is not necessary for all yarns to be twisted to the degree necessary to achieve maximum strength. Some yarns are required with soft and desirable characteristics requiring less twist, and thus having a somewhat reduced strength.

Direction of Twist Another point of great importance is the direction in which the twist is inserted in the yarn. This is merely a matter of rotating the spindle in either one direction or the other.

It is general practice to refer to these two directions as S- and Z- twist as shown in Fig. 4.12.

The downstroke of each letter indicates the direction in which the surface fibres lie.

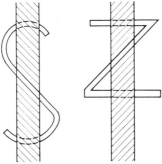

Fig. 4.12   S- and Z-twist in yarns

For some purposes it is necessary to have doubled yarns, which are single yarns twisted together. The twist of the single yarns can either run in the same, twist on twist, or in the opposite direction, twist against twist. The latter is the more common method, since when the single twists are in opposite directions the doubled yarn is smoother and more lustrous.

BULKED AND TEXTURED YARNS

In the chapter on fibre manufacture it was explained that man-made fibres are available in two forms: continuous filaments, which are twisted to give smooth surfaced continuous filament yarn, and staple, the short fibres that are used to form spun yarns with broken surfaces. When they were first developed the continuous filament synthetic yarns did not compete effectively with spun yarns, particularly those made from natural fibres, because they did not have the same hairiness, bulk and warmth of handle, or the high moisture absorbency which the spun yarns possess. However, rapid expansion since the early 1950s of yarn-bulking and texturing changed the situation.

Some of the properties of spun yarns can now be given to the continuous filament man-made yarns, which are then suitable for knitting and weaving into fabrics previously thought to be well outside their scope. Bulked yarns have already become a well-established and important part of the textile industry. The drape and handle of the fabric is altered and air spaces are developed, which can result in increased comfort and warmth.

Texturing, or bulking, is the means whereby properties once associated only with staple yarns are conferred upon the stronger continuous filament synthetics. Also some bulking processes introduce into the yarns an additional property of stretch. The improved properties are developed by the permanent introduction of crimps, coils, loops and crinkles into the straight filament by various methods. Many of these processes depend on the thermoplasticity of the filaments and their ability to be deformed and then set in the deformed state by heating and cooling. Various techniques have been developed for bringing about these filament modifications, and some methods are in more common usage than others. False twisting is by far the most important method and accounts for about three-quarters of the production.

The following techniques are available for bulking continuous filament yarns:

Air bulking
Knit-de-knit
Gear crimping
Knife-edge crimping
Stuffer-box crimping
False twisting.

Air Bulking

In Western countries most air-bulked yarns are processed under licence from du Pont, with the trade mark Taslan.

This is a purely mechanical process in which yarn is over-fed into a jet of compressed air (Fig. 4.13). The stream of air directed at the yarn causes the filaments to loop and curl so that the yarn contracts in length and increases in bulk. On emerging from the jet the tangled filaments are held in place by friction between the filaments, and a small amount of twist inserted in the yarns helps the loops to hold together and gives added stability. Yarns that are bulked in this way need not be thermoplastic since the technique does not rely on any heat-setting treatment.

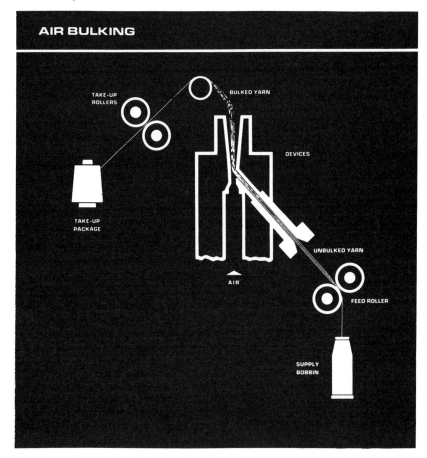

AIR BULKING

Fig. 4.13   Air bulking

The Taslan process is often used for the production of 'effect' yarns, where two or more yarns are combined. The central yarn is referred to as the 'core' yarn, and this acts as a carrier and one or more effect yarns are overfed on to the core. These yarns are fed to the air jet at a greater rate to produce bouclé or chenille effects. By varying the technique and feed rates a great variety of fancy yarns can be produced. These yarns have a low extensibility and are, therefore, used in woven fabrics.

Knit-de-Knit

A thermoplastic continuous filament yarn is knitted into a plain fabric and this is heat-set. The yarn is then unravelled from the fabric, but the knitted stitch shape is permanently set into the yarn. A crinkle yarn of this type enhances the lustre of a fabric, whereas fully bulked yarns depress the lustre. This method still only accounts for a fraction of the market but trilobal nylons (yarns with filaments of triangular rather than circular cross-section) are featuring in the use of knit-de-knit because of the lustre which the yarn possesses.

Knit-de-knit yarn gives a crêpe or bouclé effect when knitted into a fabric, but the process does not produce a stretch yarn.

A variation of the knitting technique has been developed by Heathcoat Yarns & Fibres Ltd. Knitting sinkers and a heated head are used, but no needles are used so that there is no unravelling.

Gear Crimping

A thermoplastic yarn can be crimped by passing the straight continuous filament yarn between two heated intermeshing cog wheels or some similar device. Yarns produced in this way and by the knit-de-knit process have a wavy configuration and have no tendency to twist. They are referred to as crinkle yarns.

An advantage of gear crimping is that it is a continuous process in comparison with the knit-de-knit batch-wise process involving the three stages of knitting, setting and unravelling (Fig. 4.14).

Edge Crimping

In comparison with the previous two methods when a crinkled yarn is produced, edge crimping (Fig. 4.15) results in the formation of coils in the filaments. The thermoplastic yarn is heated and drawn, as it cools, over a knife-edge. This distortion, due to sharp bending, causes one side of the individual filaments to

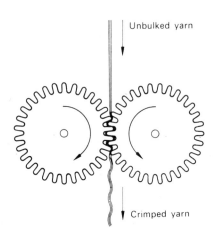

Unbulked yarn

Crimped yarn

Fig. 4.14   Gear crimping

shorten relative to the other so that they coil into a helical shape. In order to achieve the full bulking potential the yarns are then relaxed in hot water. These yarns have good stretch properties and are suitable for such end-uses as stretch nylon stockings. One of the trade marks used for this type of yarn is Agilon.

Stuffer-Box Crimping

Stuffer-box crimping (Fig. 4.16) has been developed by the Bancroft Corporation as the Ban-lon process and, in the Western countries, is the only process of its type operating under licence. The yarn is packed into a small heated box known as a stuffer box. The filaments are folded into zigzags as they are compressed into the limited volume and are then heat-set in this form; for this reason only thermoplastic yarns can be modified in this way.

The resulting yarns have a typical angular crimp and their main use for apparel is in knitted outerwear.

The False-Twist Process

Initially a batch process was carried out involving the three stages of twisting the yarn, setting in this twist and then untwisting the yarn. This was referred to as the twist–set–untwist method of bulking. However, a continuous process is now

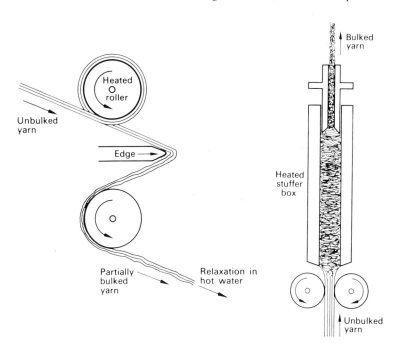

Fig. 4.15   Edge crimping   *Fig. 4.16   Stuffer-box crimping*

used employing a false-twist spindle, giving the name of false-twist bulking to the process (Fig. 4.17). Each section of yarn still undergoes the three basic stages of twisting, setting and untwisting. The thermoplastic yarn is highly twisted and then set in this form by heating and cooling. The yarn then moves on and is untwisted, by the false-twist spindle, in the opposite direction beyond the starting-point. Since the filaments were previously set in the twisted state they are unable to regain their original parallel form, and they buckle and loop.

The yarn is considerably bulked and has the property of stretch. If it is extended the filaments straighten, but if the yarn is slackened the filaments again become a tangled mass. The yarns tend to twist and it is usual to produce a double yarn in order to overcome this problem. One yarn will have the twist set in one direction, and the other yarn in the opposite direction so that a more stable yarn is obtained.

The false-twist process is often used for nylon and polyester yarns. The fabrics made from these yarns are then suitable for fitted garments with a certain amount of stretch, such as swim-suits, stockings and tights, ski pants and gloves. The

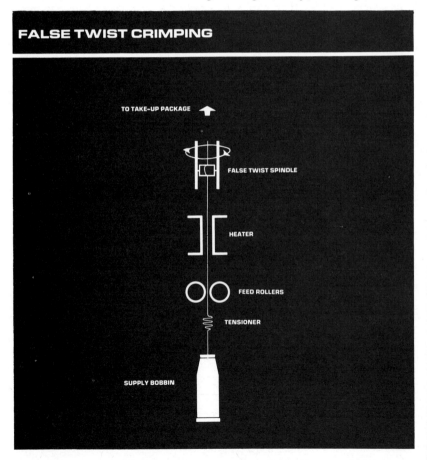

Fig. 4.17   False-twist crimping

process can be modified to give a bulked yarn, without the property of stretch, by giving an additional heat-setting treatment which stabilizes the yarn. Bulked Terylene is produced by false twisting and modified by a steaming process.

It is now common to take yarn for false twisting from the undrawn cheese and to carry out stretching and twisting on one machine. This is referred to as false-twist draw-texturizing.

The consumer is often confused by the different trade marks used and Table 4.1 endeavours to simplify the field. A short summary of the different processes is given and some well-known trade marks in each section are listed.

Bulked yarns have already become a well-established and important part of the

TABLE 4.1 BULKED AND TEXTURED YARNS

Process	Method	Trade marks (some examples)
Air bulking	The yarn is over-fed into a jet of compressed air and this causes it to loop and curl	Taslan

The following methods are dependent on the use of thermoplastic fibres:

Process	Method	Trade marks (some examples)
Knit-de-knit	A thermoplastic continuous filament yarn is heat-set in the form of a knitted fabric. The yarn is then unravelled, the knitted shape being set into it	Miralon*
Gear crimping	The yarn is passed between two heated, intermeshing cog-wheels, and thus deformed	Miralon*
Edge crimping	The yarn is heated and drawn, as it cools, over a blunt knife-edge. This causes the filaments to distort and coil, as a result of de-orientation	Agilon
Stuffer box	The yarn is compressed into a small, heated box and then fixed in the zig-zag form	Ban-lon, Tycora
Twist–set–untwist batch process	Filament yarn is given high twist, heat-fixed, and then untwisted beyond the starting-point. Two filaments are then combined, having twist in opposite directions	Helanca
False-twisting continuous process	This has largely replaced the batch method. The twisted yarn is heat-set and then untwisted using a false twist spindle	Astralon, bulked Terylene, Fluflene, Helancaset, Trevira 2000
Chemical processes	Bicomponent yarns can be made by the fibre producer. Two polymers with different shrinkage potential are spun together and the yarn given a treatment to bring about shrinkage	Orlon Type 24, Sayelle – trade mark for article with this yarn

* General trade mark for crinkle yarns by Heathcoat Yarns & Fibres Ltd.

textile industry, and it would seem likely that more man-made fibres will be produced in the form of continuous filament yarns of one kind or another. The techniques of bulking and texturing are of added significance due to the continual increase in the proportion of fabrics manufactured by various knitting techniques, for which bulked yarns are suitable. The man-made fibre producers can thus produce yarns more or less ready for weaving or knitting, without the additional processes of cutting up the extruded filaments and respinning the resulting staple on traditional textile machinery.

SPECIALITY YARNS
Effect Yarns

Special effects may be produced by using metallic or tinsel yarns, which give a sheen or degree of ornamentation to the fabric. Metallic threads may be made from gold, silver, copper, etc., and often consist of metal foil sandwiched between plastic film.

Most fancy or novelty yarns are produced by twisting together two or more yarns. The two yarns may be delivered continuously to the twisting-spindle, with one of them being delivered at a greater speed than the other. The yarn that is over-fed will obviously be in excess and will therefore wrap around the other yarn. A marl yarn is produced by combining two slubbings or rovings of different colour or lustre.

It is also possible to deliver one of the components intermittently and thus cause an accumulation of one yarn around another at certain positions along the length of the final product. These yarns will therefore have irregular knops or nodes along their length. These knops can be spaced at regular or random intervals, and their size can be controlled. Tufts of fibres may be inserted at intervals between two yarns that are being twisted together. These slubs are usually produced by intermittently feeding rovings to the twisting-spindle.

A snarl yarn is formed by feeding a highly twisted yarn at an excess rate on to the core yarn. The twist causes the slack yarn to form snarls that stand out from the fancy yarn.

Numerous variations of these techniques are possible, including the use of yarns of contrasting colours wound around one another in such a way that different colours dominate at intervals.

Bicomponent Yarns

A bicomponent fibre can be considered as a double filament in which two individual components are present. For example, in the production of the Orlon bicomponent fibre, two filaments of different chemical composition are fused together during spinning to form one double filament. This structure gives the fibre special physical characteristics. The two chemically different forms will not react in the same way when subjected to heat or moisture. On heating, one side of the fibre shrinks more than the other, thus giving the bicomponent filament a high degree of crimp. The nature of this crimp is similar to that given by wool and is different from the mechanically induced crimps described previously. The crimp can be readily developed during normal processing operations such as dyeing, followed by drying.

On wetting, one component will swell more than the other, and this will be the one on the same side as that which shrunk on heating. This side effectively elongates and decreases the crimp, but recrimping takes place on drying.

Filament Blend Yarns

Entirely new yarns are now produced by mingling together filaments of different fibres. Tricelon is produced by mingling Tricel and Celon as represented in the diagram. A new range of light-weight fabrics can be produced from this yarn, and they combine the aesthetic appeal of Tricel with the strength of nylon (Fig. 4.18).

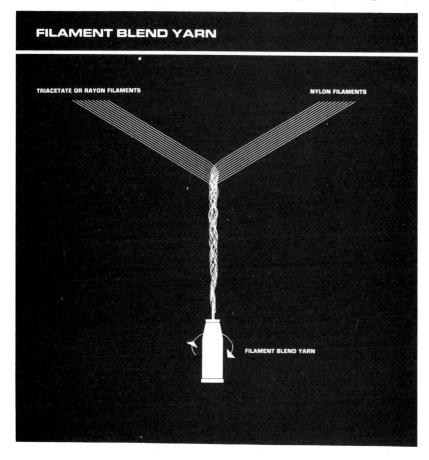

Fig. 4.18 Filament blend yarn

Filament blend yarns are also produced from acetate and nylon. Si-tussa is the trade mark used by Novaceta for their yarn of this type. Before the development of these yarns it had only been possible to blend the staple fibres, but this process represents a major breakthrough, since blended yarns can now be produced in continuous filament form.

The range of fabrics produced from Tricelon includes ninons, crêpes, georgettes, fine twills and jerseys. In order to produce crêpes with a full handle, the nylon is fully relaxed and bulks out the Tricel. Alternatively the fabric can be held out in finishing and the cloth set to give stable and smooth-surfaced materials. The woven fabrics have a rustle and scroop not unlike that of silk. They are, of course, easy-care fabrics and will not require a lot of attention after washing. They may be ironed if necessary, but on the whole have a good resistance to creasing.

Multilobal Filaments

As mentioned earlier, nylon filaments are usually produced with a circular cross-section, but fibres are now available with trilobal cross-sections. The physical and chemical characteristics are the same as the standard yarn, but the trilobal structure gives a unique highlight and sparkle effect to the fabrics produced from these yarns. Prints applied to both woven and knitted fabric have a good clarity and definition.

Other variations in cross-sections have included the production of flat ribbon-like filaments, used as decorative yarns and artificial grass.

Polyester fibres are produced with an octalobal cross-section. When standard polyester has been textured the cross-section of the fibre is basically round but with flattened sides. These flattened sides reflect the light and thus create highlight effects in the finished fabric. An octalobal fibre is used so that after texturizing the flattened sides are not present to the same extent and the glitter of the fabric is therefore reduced.

Epitropic Fibres

I.C.I. Fibres have recently introduced epitropic fibres, which conduct electricity and can thus be used to produce fabrics which never develop a high static charge. In an epitropic fibre very fine particles of carbon, a good electrical conductor, are embedded in the surface of synthetic fibres. Epitropic fibres are thus black due to the carbon but since only very small quantities of epitropic fibre are required to conduct away static – sometimes as little as one part in 500 – they are not easily seen. Both nylon and polyester are available in epitropic form. The epitropic nylon can be used in carpets to prevent static build-up and the modified polyester is suitable for industrial clothing where there is a danger of explosion.

Heterofil or Meldable Fibres

Various forms of biconstituent fibre construction are theoretically possible, but the main developments so far have involved the use of a core of one polymer covered by a skin of another. Two polymers can also be extruded side by side.

Nylon heterofil, or meldable fibres, are made by I.C.I. Fibres. They consist of a sheath of nylon 6 which has a comparatively low melting point and a core of nylon 66 with a higher melting point. Filaments are extruded from a battery of spinnerets on to a moving conveyor and laid in random fashion to form a web. This is then heated so that the filament skin of the individual fibres softens and melts, and spot bonds are formed where the heterofil fibres touch. The web is next passed to a cooling zone where the skin solidifies to form a permanent bond at each intersection. The method of fabric production varies. In some cases the web is needled and then passed through an oven to produce the inter-fibre bonds. Alternatively the web can be passed beneath a heated pressure roller. This method has the benefit that a lower processing temperature can be used and an embossed roller will produce a surface pattern on the fabric. I.C.I. Fibres have used the trade mark Cambrelle for materials produced from meldable fibres and filaments.

5. Preparation of Yarn for Fabric Manufacture

THE more traditional methods of fabric production are weaving, knitting, lace-making and felting.

Weaving is the method of fabric production by which two sets of threads are interwoven at right angles (Fig. 5.1). The process depends on taking longitudinal threads, known as the warp, and interweaving these with lateral threads, known as the weft. The manner in which the sets of yarns are interlaced affects the characteristics of the cloth; a specific manner of interlacing is known as the weave, e.g. plain, twill, satin and many other variations.

Knitting is a method of fabric construction in which the yarn is formed into loops which are connected together. In its simplest form a knitted fabric may be constructed of one continuous thread throughout. Knitted fabrics are divided into two groups, according to the method of production used. If the material is constructed of loops made from single yarns that run across the fabric, it is said to

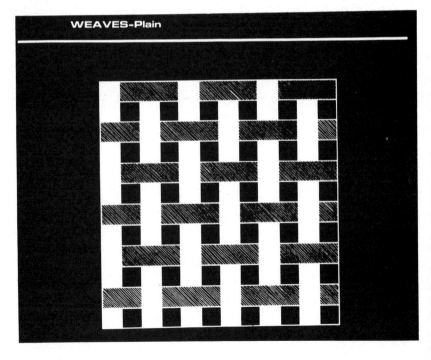

WEAVES-Plain

Fig. 5.1   The construction of a woven fabric

KNITTING – Weft

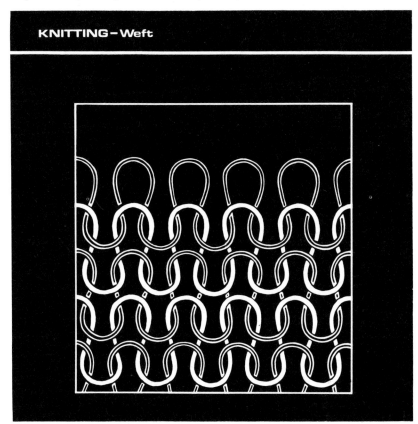

Fig. 5.2(a)   Weft knitting

be weft-knitted. It can be seen from the diagram illustrating weft knitting (Fig. 5.2(a)), that if the path of a continuous thread is followed it lies across the fabric in the weft direction. On the other hand, the fabric may be constructed from a group of yarns that run lengthwise. In this case, as illustrated (Fig. 5.2(b)), if the path of a continuous thread is followed it lies along the length of the fabric in the warp direction, and this method of construction is therefore known as warp knitting.

There are differences of opinion as to what constitutes a lace fabric, but as a general definition all lace fabrics consist entirely of sets of threads, and some of these are twisted round the others at intervals (Fig. 5.3). Lace may be produced by braiding, knotting, knitting or looping or by twisting or stitching.

Felts do not require the use of yarns in their manufacture, but they are made directly from animal hairs, such as wool, which have a surface scale structure. When a mass of such fibres is subjected to the action of moisture, heat and varying pressures, the fibres interlock and become entangled into a compact mass. This individual characteristic of the animal hair fibres is known as felting and it seems

KNITTING – Warp Knit

Fig. 5.2(b)   Warp knitting

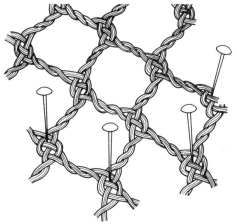

Fig. 5.3   Structure of a lace fabric – Brussels lace

almost certain that the most important factor is the presence of the scales. The tips of the scales in a wool fibre all point to the tip of the fibre, and the fibre will thus be able to move more easily through a mass of fibres backwards, in a root-first direction. Hence the fibres become entangled with one another and the mass is drawn together in a consolidated form. Some types of woollen fabric are woven first and then felted by the milling process to give a fluffy texture; for example blankets are often treated in this way. The phenomenon of felting is dealt with in greater detail in Chapter 10 when discussing fabric properties.

The two most important methods of fabric manufacture, weaving and knitting, are considered in detail in subsequent chapters. However, the yarn produced on the spinning-frame is not in the right state for cloth manufacture, and we must therefore consider the preparatory processes to which the yarn must be subjected before it is ready for use on the loom or knitting-machine. It may be necessary to twist two or more single yarns together to increase the strength or they may be folded together to make fancy yarns.

The ring tube, on to which the yarn is wound by the spinning-frame, does not contain long enough lengths of yarn for use as warp threads, and is not a convenient size as a source of weft yarn. One important preparatory process therefore involves winding the yarn on to more suitable packages.

Warping involves the production of a continuous sheet of parallel threads wound on to a beam. These are then presented to the loom in a suitable state for weaving, and are interlaced by the weft yarn. For use as warps in woven cloth much of the yarn has to have an adhesive and lubricant applied to it so as to withstand the frictions of the loom; this process is known as sizing. With many yarns that are to be used on knitting-machines it is desirable to give them an oiling treatment.

The preparatory processes can therefore be considered under the general headings of winding, warping, sizing and looming and the following diagram illustrates the sequence of the processes.

Preparatory Processes for Fabric Manufacture

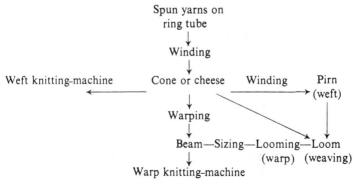

PACKAGING OR WINDING

One of the main reasons for winding warp yarns is to obtain longer lengths of yarn to permit the continuous production of long lengths of fabric. The tension of the yarn is also adjusted and faults, such as slubs and other thick places in the yarn, are removed. Devices are now available which can automatically detect yarn faults while the thread is being wound from one package to another. The yarn then breaks, the fault is removed, and the two ends reconnected. It is essential that the number of yarn breakages is kept to a minimum on the loom. When breakages do occur, the broken ends or picks, the warp or weft threads, must be reconnected and the loom restarted. The economics of weaving are closely related to the number of breakages, because if these are numerous the production rate of the loom will be reduced and much of the weaver's time will be taken up in reconnecting and restarting the loom.

The lengths of yarn are wound on to special packages such as cheeses and cones, which consist of a paper or wooden core without flanges. Cheeses are suitable for many purposes, but the cone package is particularly suited to soft-spun yarns and for hosiery manufacture, on circular knitting-machines.

The winding of weft yarns for use on conventional weaving looms is then dependent on producing a package which is suitable for using in the shuttle, and this usually means winding the yarn on to pirns. In the production of the warp yarns it has already been mentioned that the aim is to produce long lengths so that continuous production of fabrics can be maintained. However, in the preparation of the weft on the pirn the reverse is the case and the yarn is generally wound from long lengths into shorter lengths. Weft yarns must fit into the shuttle and then be thrown across the loom in order to insert the weft, at right angles to the warp threads. The size of package which can be used is therefore limited by the design of the traditional loom. Newer looms are designed to replace the empty pirns by automatic processes and, more recently, modified so that a larger supply package can be used. In these cases the weft is carried across the loom by alternative methods, but the supply package remains stationary. The looms will be discussed in detail in the next chapter and have only been mentioned here in so far as they require different supply packages.

WARPING

The aim of warping is to produce a sheet of parallel yarns from the various supply packages. These yarns must be of great length and also be evenly spaced. Several hundred packages are placed in a creel, which consists of a series of vertical bars, that hold the packages in position, but allow them to rotate for the yarn to be wound off. The yarns pass from the packages on the creel through a reed, a type of comb, which separates the individual yarns. The spaces between this comb are called the dents. After passing through this reed, the threads then go over a measuring roller, are tensioned and pass through an expanding reed. The expanding reed spaces the yarns uniformly. The machine which carries out the process is known as a beam warper and the yarns are spread out evenly to cover the length of the beam (Fig. 5.4).

Fig. 5.4 High-speed warping. Yarn from the two sides of the creel is being fed to the beam in the foreground

A normal beam usually contains several thousand ends. However the capacity of a creel is normally limited to 900 packages or less because of space considerations and it is therefore impossible to wind the beam required at the loom in one stage. One method of overcoming this difficulty is to prepare several back beams or warper's beams, all the yarns being of the required length and when added together these give the required number of warp ends.

The operation of sizing the sheet of yarns from the back beams and winding them on to the weaver's beam is known as slashing. At this stage yarns are also added at either side and the selvedge will be produced from these.

However, it is also possible to wind one group of warp threads and then wind the next group. All the blocks are eventually placed side by side across the width of the beam and make up together the number of ends required in the final fabric. This process is known as section warping and is often used for coloured yarns and for worsted and woollen yarns. The same principles apply and the yarn is taken from the supply packages on a creel.

Devices are available that will stop the machine if a yarn breaks.

SIZING

Stresses are imposed on the yarns during weaving and most of the warps would completely break down and prevent weaving if they were not sized. The purpose of sizing is therefore to apply a protective coating against abrasion. It also prevents broken filament yarns bending back and being woven in. In an unsized spun warp projecting fibres would become trapped between neighbouring ends. The fibres must be held together to form a compact thread, and there must not be any projecting hairs. The warp yarns therefore must have a smooth surface. Warp-sizing involves the application of an adhesive to the warp before weaving. A lubricant and other substance may be added, and the aim is to prevent the disruption of the yarns as a result of the weaving process. The mixture of substances applied is called the size.

As explained, the adhesive provides a protective coating against abrasion and binds the fibres together. The lubricant reduces the friction at contact points between yarns and the other additives may be used for tinting or weighting, or an antiseptic substance may be added to prevent mildew or bacterial action on the yarns.

It is essential that the size can be removed readily before bleaching and dyeing the fabric.

The quantity of size to be added to the yarns is critical. Too little means that the yarns are unable to withstand the stresses of weaving and breakages occur. Too much means that breakages occur due to the lumps when size accumulates on natural slubs.

Suitable sizes include such substances as starch, gelatine and the modern synthetic resins – polyvinyl alcohol, polyvinyl acetate and polyacrylic acid types. Lubricants include tallow and paraffin waxes together with synthetic materials to give good lubrication with antistatic properties and easy removal during finishing. The substances chosen and the relative proportions used vary according to the type of fibre being processed (cotton, acetate, nylon, etc.) and whether it is a filament or spun yarn. Woollen and worsted yarns are not usually sized.

Application of the Size

The warps from the back beams are drawn forward to produce a continuous sheet of yarns and passed into the size box, which contains the hot sizing mixture. The yarns pass under the submerging roller and then between a pair of rollers, which squeeze out the excess size. The sized yarn is then dried by passing over large-diameter drying cylinders, which are steam-heated, or through an air-drying machine (Fig. 5.5). Care must be taken to keep all the warp threads separate, and no two warps must be joined together by size. Rods are used to split the yarns, and they are then passed through a reed with spaced wires. The warp is finally passed round a measuring roller and wound on to the weaver's beam. At this point the length of the warp is often marked at intervals as a guide to the weaver.

LOOMING

The final stage in preparing for weaving is known as looming, the process by which the warp yarns from the beam at the back of the loom are drawn forward

Fig. 5.5   Slasher sizing machine fitted with computerized controls. The sheet of warp yarn is passed through the size solution. It is then dried and the yarns separated and then wound on to a weaver's beam

through the eyes of the healds and through the dents of the reed (Fig. 5.6). There are essentially three types of machine.

Knotting Machines   These are used when a new warp is to be used on the loom that is identical to the previous one. In this case the knotting machine connects the new warp to the ends of the similar one, on the loom.

However, when a new warp is to be used the process is more complicated.

Drawing-in Machines   The needle automatically selects each warp end and draws it through the eye of the heald and through a dent in the reed.

Reaching Machines   These machines select each end automatically and the operative does the actual drawing through.

Without the aid of these machines looming has to be done manually by two operatives. The weaver's beam, the healds ('needles') and the reed are placed in a frame and one of the operatives, the 'reacher-in', selects the warp threads individually and in the correct order as defined by the weaving pattern. A hook is passed through the eye of the heald by the 'drawer-in'. This holds the warp thread and as it is withdrawn pulls the yarn through the eye of the heald. This process of drawing-in manually is extremely tedious and monotonous, but sometimes it is still carried out in this way. The yarns are then passed through the dents of the reed.

The weaver's beam, plus the heald shafts and reed, are then fitted in the loom and 'gaited-up'. The loom is then ready for weaving.

Fig. 5.6   Looming – drawing the ends through the healds

6. Fabric Manufacture: Weaving

Woven fabric comprises two sets of yarns: warp threads running along the length of the cloth and weft threads, which lie across the fabric at right angles to the warp. Weaving is the method of interlacing these two sets of yarns and the machine used for carrying out this operation is called a loom, of which there are many different types (Figs 6.1 and 6.2).

THE CONVENTIONAL LOOM AND THE METHOD OF WEAVING

Warp threads from a weaver's beam at the back of the loom are passed over a back-rest and then horizontally forward. They are separated by lease rods to prevent them from becoming tangled together, before passing through the loom harness. This harness is made up of a number of heald frames, each carrying heald wires with an eye through which the warp thread passes. The purpose of the heald frames is to control the raising and lowering of warp threads throughout weaving.

During a preparatory process, i.e. looming or gaiting-up, each warp thread is selected and threaded through a particular heald eye to a predetermined pattern, so that all the threads allocated to any one of the available heald frames rise and fall together.

After passing through the heald frames the warp threads are carried through a reed. This is a metal comb extending across the width of the loom and serves, among other things, to keep the warp threads evenly spaced across the cloth. In front of the reed is the point known as the 'fell' of the cloth, where warp and weft eventually combine to produce a woven fabric.

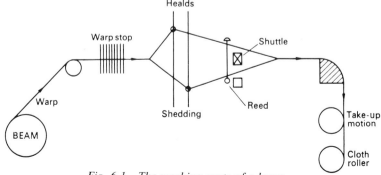

Fig. 6.1   The working parts of a loom

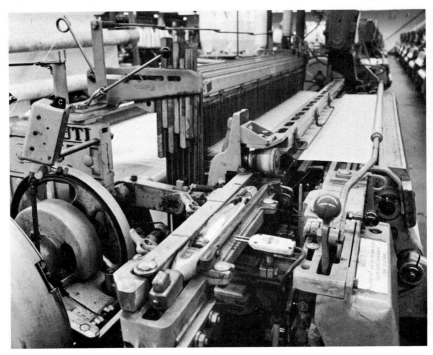

Fig. 6.2   The loom set up for weaving. (By courtesy of the Textile Council)

Weft threads are introduced at a point between the reed and the fell of the cloth. In a conventional loom a shuttle carrying a weft supply package is propelled across the warp from side to side leaving a single weft thread trail lying at right angles to the warp threads. It is, of course, essential that each single insertion of weft, commonly referred to as a 'pick' of weft, is interlaced with the warp threads. This is achieved by the 'shedding' action of the heald frames mentioned above: those frames which are raised will lift their corresponding warp threads to form an upper sheet of warp, while those which are lowered will form a bottom sheet. The space between the two sheets of warp is called a 'shed', hence the term 'shedding'. The shuttle is now propelled through the shed, laying one pick of weft between the upper and lower warp sheets, an action called 'picking'.

Before another pick can be inserted, the first pick has to undergo a 'beating-up' action, so that it is pressed firmly up against the fell of the cloth, and this is quickly followed by another 'shedding' action. The effect of these two actions is to position the first pick correctly in the cloth and then bring about the interchange of the upper and lower warp sheets in readiness for the next pick. The interchange of upper and lower sheets normally means that some or all of the upper warp threads in the first shed pass to the lower sheet and vice versa, so that the next pick interlaces with the warp threads in a different order. The order of interlacing depends upon the number of healds employed in a loom and the order in which they are lifted.

Fig. 6.3   The shuttle entering the shed, i.e. travelling to the right of the picture

Weaving can therefore be summarized as a repetition of the following sequence of actions:

(1) Shedding: the warp threads are separated by raising and lowering the heald frames to form a shed, through which the shuttle can pass.
(2) Picking: the shuttle, carrying the weft, is propelled across the loom, through the shed (Fig. 6.3).
(3) Beating-up: the inserted weft yarn is pushed up against the fell of the cloth by the reed.

As the operations proceed the warp is unwound from the weaver's beam and the fabric is rolled, or 'taken-up' on to the cloth roller. By controlling the rate at which the cloth is taken-up, the required number of weft threads per centimetre can be inserted.

Although the complete sequence of shedding, picking and beating-up takes place rapidly, the number of weft threads inserted per minute will depend on many variables, including the type of loom, cloth width and the yarn to be woven. On conventional looms the rate is usually within the range 80–250 picks per minute.

As already stated, the order of interlacing warp and weft threads is controlled by the shedding motion, and the weaves which can be produced by varying the heald lifting order are described in more detail at the end of this chapter. Although the simpler weaves can be produced on tappet looms, which have a very simple mechanism for operating the healds, the more complex weaves require a more complicated mechanism for raising and lowering the warp threads. These are the dobby, for use where complex designs are required, and the Jacquard, for the production of very detailed woven designs.

Dobby   The dobby mechanism can control a large number of shafts or healds by means of a rotating pattern drum at the side of the loom. This drum has slots in it, into which pegs can be fitted, the number of slots corresponding to the number of shafts. Where the slots are empty, hooks can enter, but if pegs are in the holes the hooks are unable to enter. Whether or not the hooks are able to move into a slot controls the movement of the shaft, and only certain shafts will be raised. The drum turns after every pick and a new group of shafts is raised. Eventually the drum will return to its starting-point and the 'repeat' of the design is completed. The drum then begins another rotation.

The repeat of the design is the number of ends and picks required to produce one complete pattern. The repeat must be fairly small, and is controlled by the diameter of the drum. It is therefore possible to produce fairly complex weaves using the dobby mechanism.

An older type of dobby consists of strips of wood containing pegs, which come into contact with levers that control the raising of the shafts. A peg is inserted whenever the design requires that the warp yarn shall appear on the surface of the fabric, the number of strips of wood being equal to the number of picks in one repeat of the design.

Jacquard   To produce very ornate patterns it is necessary to be able to control each individual warp thread, and this can be done by means of a Jacquard mechanism (Fig. 6.4).

Each warp thread is drawn through a heald eye as in other methods of weaving. The heald on a Jacquard loom consists of an eye, which is weighted to hold it in position, attached to a specially treated cord. The cords run upwards to a perforated board which keeps them parallel, each cord passing through a separate hole. When the pattern does not repeat across the width of the cloth each cord lifts one thread, but where the pattern does repeat the cords from all the warp threads which are lifted at the same time are tied together. Horizontal needles in the upper part of the loom are pressed against a card by means of a spring. Each cord is attached to a rod and then passes through the eye of a needle. The upper ends of these rods are hooked and rest over a series of bars called griffes.

The warp threads which must be raised for the insertion of each pick are controlled by the needles pushing up against the cards. Where the card has been perforated the needle can pass through the small hole and will thus remain in position when the card is pressed against it. The hooks remain on the griffe, and when the griffe rises, the corresponding cords and warp ends will also rise. However, where there is no hole the card will push back the horizontal needle and tilt the rods, so that the cord to which they are attached will not raise the particular warp ends. A shed is formed between the warp ends which are raised and those which are not, and a pick is inserted.

After a Jacquard pattern has been designed and worked out, a perforated card must then be prepared for every weft thread in one repeat of the design. The cards are punched with rows of holes, each one corresponding to a warp thread which

Fig. 6.4   A Jacquard loom

must be raised. These cards are then laced together to form an endless chain and placed in a frame over the loom.

Intricate designs such as damasks (see p. 102) can be produced on Jacquard looms, but the working-out of the design and the preparation of the loom and cards take a long time and explain the high price of such fabrics.

THE IMPROVEMENT OF CONVENTIONAL LOOMS AND THE DEVELOPMENT OF NEW METHODS OF INSERTING THE WEFT

A Summary of the Recent Developments in Automatic and Shuttleless Looms

In the past a lot of time and effort was devoted to improving the conventional loom rather than to developing radically new forms of machinery. The industry was able to employ numbers of people fairly easily and was labour intensive, but could not spend vast amounts of capital on machinery. However, in recent years with the increasing amount of competition in the market, plus the influence of labour shortages, high wages and increased costs, there has been a reversal of the situation. These changes resulted in much re-equipment, and vast sums of money are now invested in machinery. There has thus been an incentive for more research and experimentation to develop new machinery, aiming at automation and increased production speeds, with a reduction in the number of operatives required.

Much of this development has been based on the traditional shuttle-type loom which has been improved by developing methods of automatically replenishing the weft. Weaving speeds are fairly high and the machine requires less supervision. One operative can look after a large number of machines and the labour costs are therefore reduced. The modern automatic loom now predominates in most branches of the weaving industry for this reason, plus the fact that it is an efficient and reliable machine, which can be used to produce a wide range of fabrics.

In recent years more unorthodox machines have been developed in which new methods of weft insertion are employed. These are based mainly on the idea that really high-speed weaving can only be achieved by modifications which reduce the weight and number of heavy reciprocating parts in the loom. The weft is therefore inserted from a bulk supply and the conventional shuttle is replaced by an alternative, carefully controlled method of insertion. Some of these new machines are already established and are widely used, while others are only in the experimental stages. These new machines are often referred to as shuttleless looms, and these can be considered in two sections according to whether a direct or indirect method of weft insertion is employed (Fig. 6.5).

One indirect method of weft insertion is based on the rapier principle. Two carriers from each side of the loom meet half-way across the shed and the yarn is transferred from one to the other. An even more outstanding example is the Sulzer weaving machine where the weft is inserted by means of a small gripper-projectile which is projected across the loom through the warp shed at high speed.

The more unorthodox looms are based on direct weft insertion; examples are looms in which the weft is propelled across the loom by means of air or water jets. The advantages of these looms are the high speeds at which the picks can be inserted and the reduction in noise of the operation. However, the fabric width is somewhat limited as is the type of yarn that can be used.

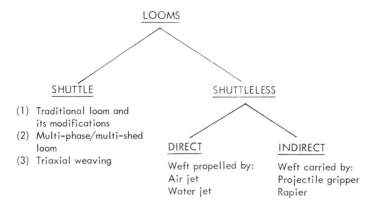

Fig. 6.5   Loom types

The possibility of inserting the weft by methods based on solid friction, when the yarn is projected through the nip of revolving rollers, has been investigated, but the method has not been applied commercially. Electromagnetic propulsion of the shuttle has also been studied.

Improvements to the Conventional Automatic Loom

Bobbin Loaders   As has already been explained, modifications have been developed which reduce the manual tasks involved in the running of automatic looms, and replace them by mechanized processes. One such job is replacing the supply of weft yarn at regular intervals as it is used up on the loom. Obviously if larger quantities of weft were supplied at the loom the operatives would have to replenish each one less frequently and fewer operatives would therefore be required to look after a given number of machines. Such mechanization has the added advantage that the reduced handling of the pirns avoids damage to the yarns and can result in improved cloth quality. It is for these reasons that the bobbin loader has been introduced, to replace the conventional weft battery on the loom. The special boxes are of large capacity and are automatically packed with pirns at the winding frame, with all the heads to the same side. These containers hold between 72 and 180 pirns and it is usual to have two containers at each loom. The amount of reserve weft yarn is therefore far greater than in the conventional circular magazine which only holds about two dozen pirns. The pirns are supplied direct to the weft transfer mechanism as required. They pass through the shutter opening in the container to the pirn guide, and the pirn is then transferred to the shuttle. The complete preparation of a new pirn takes about five seconds.

Weft Winding at the Loom   The bobbin loader described above saves labour and reduces costs by supplying a large quantity of reserve weft, but the complete solution to the problem would be to wind the pirns directly on the loom, from

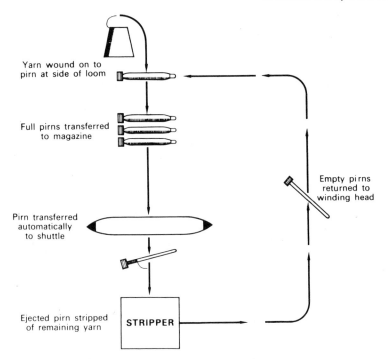

Yarn wound on to
pirn at side of loom

Full pirns transferred
to magazine

Empty pirns
returned to
winding head

Pirn transferred
automatically
to shuttle

Ejected pirn stripped
of remaining yarn

STRIPPER

Fig. 6.6   Weft winding at the loom

large packages (Fig. 6.6). This is the basis of the development of the 'Unifil' loom winder, introduced by the Leesona Corporation.

The weft is supplied on a large package and is then wound on to the pirn at the winding head at the side of the loom. A fully wound pirn is transferred automatically to a magazine which holds five or six pirns. These are fed into the shuttle as required by the normal pirn-changing mechanism, and the used pirn is ejected from the shuttle and fed to a stripper, which removes any remaining yarn. The cleaned pirns are then carried by a conveyor back up to the winding head, where they are rewound with weft yarn ready to be used again.

None of the equipment and labour in the winding room is required and the pirns do not have to be transported between the two departments. With a loom winder only a fairly small number of pirns, perhaps about twelve, is needed for each loom, in comparison to the two or three hundred required for a conventional loom; the amount of capital represented by the pirns being greatly reduced.

The 'Unifil' loom winder can therefore provide a considerable saving in manpower, the only action required by the operatives being the replacement of the weft supply packages and the tying in of ends when the yarn is broken.

Circular Weaving   Some designers have worked to produce a circular weaving machine which has the advantage that the weft is inserted by a complete rotary motion. This means that the shuttle can be in continuous operation in a circular path, and indeed it is possible to have several shuttles in use at the same time, each inserting weft yarns. The fact that the motion is continuous and in one direction reduces wear and tear, and results in a more uniform weft tension. Although much work has been carried out to develop this principle and circular weaving machines have been produced there are still only a few in operation.

New Methods of Inserting the Weft

Weft Insertion by the Rapier Principle This method of weft insertion aims at obtaining high-speed weaving. The weft-insertion system is based on a modified rapier principle. Two carriers move through the warp shed simultaneously from each side of the loom and meet approximately half-way across the shed. The weft is supplied from cones on the right-hand side only, and is thus fed to the right-hand carrier. When the carriers meet the weft yarn is transferred from the right-hand carrier to the left-hand carrier and they then reverse direction and return to the sides of the loom again. The weft thread has thus been carried across the loom and one pick has been inserted. Although the warp shed changes after each pick, the weft is laid in cycles of two picks, with loops joining the two on the right-hand side of the cloth. There will thus be a uniform selvedge on this side and all the open ends will be on the left-hand side. Then these are bound together with separate selvedge yarns (Fig. 6.7).

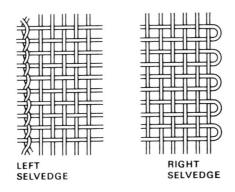

**LEFT
SELVEDGE**

**RIGHT
SELVEDGE**

Fig. 6.7 Selvedges from rapier loom

After the first pick of the two-pick cycle has been inserted and the carrier enters the shed again for the second pick, the cutter, through which the yarn is passed, closes and cuts the weft thread to the correct length. The supply of weft yarn is then held by the gripper, the cut portion is carried across the shed, and the insertion of the second pick is completed. The cycle is then repeated. This rapier system of weft insertion has been successfully adopted and is suitable for the production of the simpler types of fabric, which use one type of weft thread, and are normally produced on single-shuttle looms.

Sulzer Shuttleless Weaving Machine In the Sulzer machine the weft is carried through the shed by a small projectile, weighing about 30 g. The weft is again supplied from a package at the side of the machine. The gripper carries the yarn from one side to the other side of the machine, and thus inserts the pick.

Obviously the energy required for this is a great deal less than that required to propel the larger and heavier conventional shuttle across the loom. All the picks are delivered from the same side of the machine as the supply package and thus, after a pick has been inserted, the gripper is brought to rest and eventually passed back across the loom by a slow-moving conveyor, for using again. In the machine 330 cm wide there are seventeen grippers. The Sulzer weaving machine produces a tuck-in selvedge, by drawing the cut weft end into the same shed (Fig. 6.8).

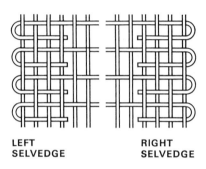

LEFT   **RIGHT**
SELVEDGE   **SELVEDGE**

Fig. 6.8   Selvedges from Sulzer loom

The 330 cm machine is found to be the most competitive width due to economic considerations, and productivity is high.

More Unconventional Methods of Weft Insertion   An even more exciting development has been the introduction of weaving machines in which any form of yarn carrier has been eliminated. One of these is the air-jet machine. A special device measures off the correct length of weft depending on the width of the cloth to be woven, and a jet of air carries the weft through the warp shed.

An alternative method of carrying the weft across the machine is by the use of a water jet. Again, a measuring device unwinds sufficient yarn for one pick from the supply package. A pump then forces water into a nozzle and the water pressure is thus built up, opens the nozzle and a fine jet of water is projected into the warp shed. This jet carries the weft with it, and will stop when the reserve quantity of weft, that has been unwound, has been used up (Fig. 6.9).

In the multi-phase/multi-shed weaving system several weft ends are inserted across the full width of the warp sheet simultaneously. The weft carriers travel across the warp sheet at constant speed, spaced at regular intervals. Groups of warp ends are made to perform shed changes successively in accordance with the progress of the weft carriers. The resultant effect is that of progressing waves of warp ends as they envelope the weft carriers.

All these new developments in weaving machinery illustrate the great progress that is being made in this field and indicate the possible direction of future advance.

Fig. 6.9   A weaving shed equipped with modern water-jet looms

FABRIC STRUCTURES: WEAVES

As was explained in the section on the loom, the weave of a fabric is controlled by the shedding action. All the warp threads that have been raised in the formation of the shed will be above the pick when it is inserted, and thus these warp threads will be on the top surface of the fabric. The others will be in the lower part of the shed and the pick will pass over the top of them. The different weaves are produced by controlling the raising of the warp threads, so that only specific ends are raised for the insertion of each pick. The number of ends and picks required to produce one complete pattern in the design is known as the repeat.

There are three basic weaves, the plain weave, the twill weave and the satin weave. The variety of different woven structures is very great, but it is only possible in this text to discuss the three fundamental weaves and some of the variations of these, restricting this to the simpler and more important ones.

Plain Weave and Variations

The plain weave is woven on the one up and one down principle and the weft thread then passes over one end, under the next, over the next and so on. This is repeated in the next pick but the position of the ends is reversed so that different warp threads are on the surface.

The plain weave can give variations when two or more adjacent ends are lifted at the same time and two or more picks are inserted in the same shed. These are illustrated in Fig. 6.10 and include mat or hopsack weaves.

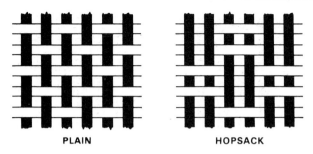

PLAIN   **HOPSACK**

Fig. 6.10   Variation on the plain weave

In a repp fabric, alternate coarse and fine ends are woven together using alternate coarse and fine picks. Where the thick ends cross the thick picks a ribbed effect is obtained.

The term poplin is usually used nowadays to describe an all-cotton fabric in which there are more ends per centimetre than picks per centimetre. Usually the ratio is about 2:1. The weft yarn is usually coarser and this means that fine ribs run across the fabric. If fibres other than cotton are present then this is usually referred to in the fabric description, i.e. Terylene/cotton poplin.

Other plain weaves include taffeta, poult and grosgrain. All these fabrics are used in the dress and blouse trade, and taffeta is particularly used as a lining fabric.

Weaves are usually indicated on design paper. If the warp thread passes above the weft thread the square is filled in, and if the weft thread is above the warp thread then the square is left blank. Thus a plain weave could be transferred to design paper as in Fig. 6.11.

The fact that a certain fabric is described as a plain rib defines the way in which the yarns are interlaced, but this may not be referring to the appearance of the cloth. Plain-weave fabrics can be decorated by the use of coloured yarns, or bright prints may be applied.

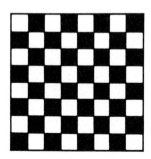

Fig. 6.11   Square diagram of plain weave

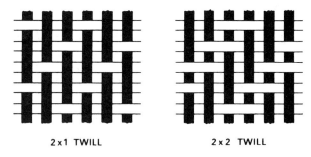

2x1 TWILL   2x2 TWILL

Fig. 6.12   Twill weaves

Twill Weave and Variations

Twill weaves are constructed by varying the order of interlacing the yarns so that diagonal lines are produced across the fabric. This is best illustrated by Fig. 6.12.

A float is produced when a given yarn is on the surface of the fabric. A weft float is produced when a weft thread passes over several successive ends in a given pick. A warp float is produced when the weft thread passes under the same end in successive picks. In a twill weave both of these floats may be present but the essential feature is the fact that they are so arranged in position that diagonal patterns are produced across the fabric. Either the warp or the weft may predominate on the surface.

Twills are often described in a numerical way. The length of warp float, the number of weft threads covered, is followed by the length of weft float, the number of warp threads covered (e.g. 2/1 twill, 3/3 twill and 1/2 twill). It must be noted that warp and weft floats on the front surface of a fabric will coincide with weft and warp floats on the back; thus a 2/1 twill on the face will be a 1/2 twill on the reverse side.

The interlacing of warp and weft threads is therefore less frequent than in a plain weave and hence softer fabrics can be produced. Since there are less intersections there can be more ends and picks per centimetre, producing a thicker cloth.

Satin and Sateen Weaves

These weaves have yarn floats on the surface of the fabric, but these are not arranged to give diagonal patterning as in the twill weave. Satin and sateen fabrics have a smooth, lustrous appearance, and top-quality fabrics are used for evening and bridal gowns. Satin linings are also produced using continuous filament yarns.

When there are warp floats on the face of the fabric, this is termed a satin. However, if the weft is mainly on the surface, then this is a sateen weave. The fact

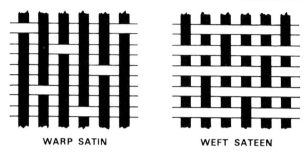

WARP SATIN   WEFT SATEEN

Fig. 6.13   Satin and sateen weaves

that there is a large predominance of one set of threads on the face gives a smooth surface effect (Fig. 6.13).

Attractive designs can be produced by having alternate blocks of satin and sateen weave. Damask is a figured fabric in which warp satin and weft sateen weaves interchange. Twill or other weaves are sometimes introduced.

Pile Fabrics

Weft-pile fabrics are called velveteens, and warp-pile fabrics are termed velvets.

A velveteen fabric is made up of a ground weave and in addition a large number of weft floats. After the fabric has been woven the surface floats are cut and brushed upright. A pile fabric is thus produced.

In order to produce a velvet having a warp pile it is necessary to use two beams in the loom: one beam for ground warp and the other for the pile warp. A special loom is used; the pile warp is interlaced with the ground warp but wire of the correct size is inserted under the pile warp, and loops or floats are thus produced. As the wire is withdrawn the loops are cut and the pile is formed. Warp velvet can also be made as a double fabric with the pile between the two sections. As the pile is cut, two cloths are produced, face to face.

Corduroy, like velveteen, is a weft-pile fabric in which the cut weft forms the surface. However, in a corduroy the binding points of the pile wefts are so arranged that once the pile has been cut, cords or ribs are formed in the warp direction. This differs from the velveteen where the binding points of the cut pile are evenly spaced.

7. Fabric Manufacture: Knitting

HAND-knitting is an ancient art, probably dating back to pre-Christian times, though it was introduced into Britain in the fifteenth century and Queen Elizabeth I was known to have quantities of knitted stockings. In hand-knitting one continuous thread is used and a stitch is made when a loop of yarn or thread is drawn through a previously made loop.

Machine-knitting is a fairly recent development compared with weaving, but the techniques have improved rapidly and it is now a very important method of fabric construction. The fabric is produced by forming the yarn into loops, each loop depending on the others near to it. A characteristic of knitted fabrics is that they will stretch and recover.

The first knitting-machine, invented by the Reverend William Lee, was built in Nottingham in 1598. However, the Reverend Lee was not given a patent for the machine and he therefore went to France and developed a machine-knitting industry around Rouen. It is reported that his brother brought many of the machines back to England. During the seventeenth century large numbers of stocking frames were in operation in many districts, including the areas around Nottingham, Leicester and London. Since that time many different types of knitting-machine have been developed and the range is now extensive. In this book it is only possible to cover the basic principles of the various types.

THE DIFFERENT KNITTING CONSTRUCTIONS

The fabric may be constructed from a single yarn or thread and the loops made horizontally across the fabric. This is called weft knitting since the thread passes across the fabric (Fig. 7.1(a)). The alternative method of knitting fabric is where at least one thread is supplied to each needle and the threads formed into loops which run lengthwise in the fabric. This is called warp knitting (Fig. 7.1(b)).

In a knitted fabric the lengthwise rows of loops are known as wales, and the rows running across the fabric are referred to as courses. When trying to follow the path of the yarn in a knitted structure, it is often easier to do this on the back of the fabric.

It is possible to classify weft-knitted fabrics according to the type of stitch, and there are three basic structures: plain, rib and purl.

Plain Knitting The plain stitch forms the fundamental structure of knitted fabrics, the stitches lying side by side in the same plane. All the loops are drawn to the same side of the fabric, every loop being drawn from the back to the face of the

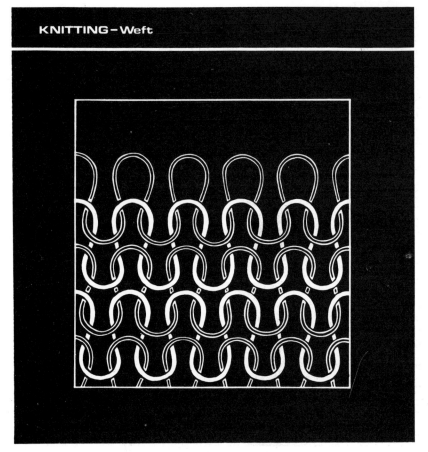

Fig. 7.1 (a)   Weft-knitted structure

fabric through loops in the previous row. Figure 7.2 illustrates the difference in appearance between the face and back of the fabric.

The back of the fabric shows a series of courses running across the fabric, and these are formed by the semicircular parts of the loops. However, on the face of the material there are V-shaped stitches, where the sides of the loops form a longitudinal line down the fabric. The V-shaped stitch on the face gives the typical appearance of classic knitwear and a smoother surface than the back. The amount of stretch which a fabric possesses depends on the yarn used and the length of yarn per stitch, but normally a plain-knit fabric will have up to 40 per cent stretch in a widthways direction.

Plain-knitted fabrics can be unravelled fairly easily. If a stitch is broken, the wale of which it is a part will break and the stitch will 'run' to produce the well-known so-called runs or ladders, and this is a certain disadvantage of the simple looped structure. A further problem is often encountered during making-up. When a plain-knitted fabric is cut it tends to curl up, due to the fact that there is

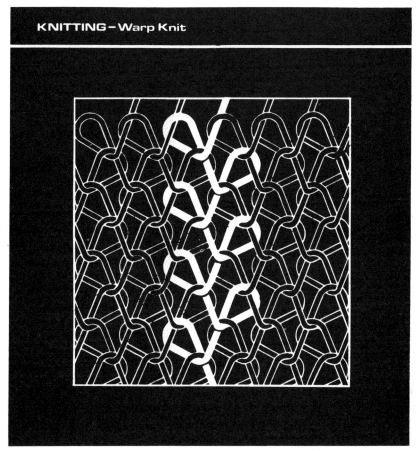

Fig. 7.1(b)   Warp-knitted structure

Courses

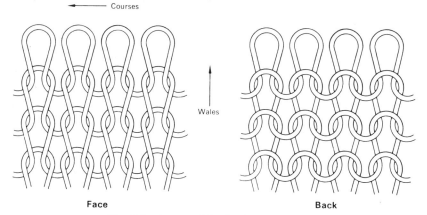

Wales

Face   Back

Fig. 7.2   Face and back of plain knitting

an unequal loop tension on the front and back of the fabric, and this makes handling rather difficult.

Rib Structure   The rib stitch is made of the same type of loop as the plain stitch, but whereas in the plain structure every loop is drawn from the back to the face, in the rib structure the loops of the same course are drawn to both sides of the fabric. Some loops are knitted to the front and others to the back.

The simplest form of this structure is the 1/1 (one and one) rib. This is illustrated in Fig. 7.3, where alternate loops in a given course are knitted to the front and back respectively. In the next course those brought to the front in the previous course are again knitted to the front, so that alternate wales will have all loops knitted to the front. The other wales will have all loops knitted to the back.

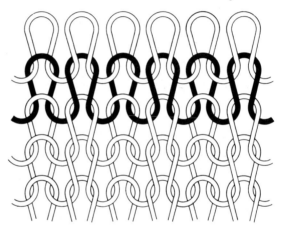

Fig. 7.3   The rib structure

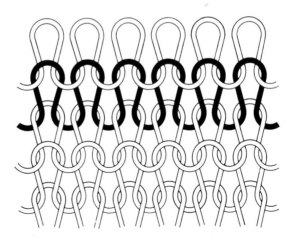

Fig. 7.4   Purl knitting

The stitches thus lie in two planes, some on the front and some on the back, and the structure is thicker than a plain-knitted fabric. The ribs, or wales, knitted in one plane tend to close up to form a double-faced fabric, and hence this structure may be referred to as double jersey.

This fabric has an equal loop tension on each side of the fabric and will not curl when cut, and, with the exception of the end knitted last, will not unravel or ladder.

Purl Knitting The same type of loop is also used in purl knitting, but successive courses of loops are drawn to opposite sides of the fabric. Thus all the loops in some courses will be drawn to the front of the fabric and all loops in the other courses to the back, so that ridges are produced, which run across the fabric. The simplest purl construction is made up of one row of loops knitted on the face of the fabric and the next row on the back. This structure has a characteristic lengthwise stretch, a property that can be used to advantage in certain articles. Purl knitting has no tendency to curl when cut, since there is again an equal loop tension on each side of the fabric, but it can be unroved from either end. Various purl designs can be made by using front and back knitting to produce a pattern (Fig. 7.4).

The knitted fabric can be patterned and decorated in many different ways by: (i) using different types of yarns, possibly of different colours; (ii) varying the method of loop formation.

(i) Different threads in varying colours may be used and the simplest method of introducing a pattern is to use different-coloured yarns for different courses. This gives a material with horizontal stripes.

Knitting can also be carried out with two separate yarns, one being seen on the face of the fabric and the other on the back. The way in which a particular coloured yarn is selected is called plating, and a colour change is brought about by reversing the position of the two yarns. Another method of introducing colour patterns is to knit the decorating yarn only on certain needles, and then to allow it to float at the back of the fabric. A float stitch is really a missed stitch, when the

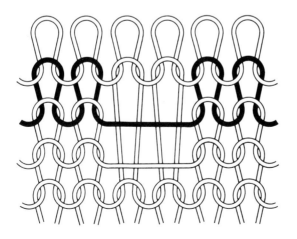

Fig. 7.5   Held stitch with floats

needle retains the old loop and fails to take a new loop. A float stitch, therefore, consists of a held loop and a short, horizontal floating thread (Fig. 7.5).

Care has to be taken in designing these fabrics to ensure that the floats are not too long, or they would catch easily.

Float stitches made on alternate needles give a structure with reduced elasticity and the end first knitted is prevented from laddering.

The complicated coloured patterns called Jacquard designs are produced by a system of knitting and missing. The loops are carefully selected so that only certain needles knit.

(ii) In addition to colour variations the knitted structure can also be decorated by varying the loop formation, either by accumulating several loops together, known as tucking, or by removing loops as in openwork or the lace stitch.

The Tuck Stitch   The tuck stitch is really an incompletely knitted loop. The needle rises to take a new loop without casting off the old one. Thus both old and new loops are held until the next course of knitting (Fig. 7.6).

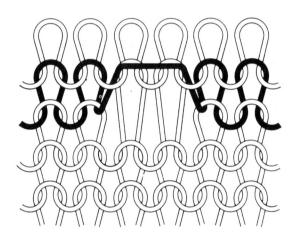

Fig. 7.6   The tuck stitch

The tucked loop is held at the back of the fabric and the long 'held' loop shows on the front of the material.

The Lace Stitch   Plain-knitted fabric forms the basic structure of a lace fabric and the lace holes are made by transferring certain loops from their correct needles to other needles, either to the left or right side, after the course of loops has been completed. This means that holes are produced in the fabric and by controlling the transfer of the loops to new needles according to a carefully predetermined pattern, interesting and attractive designs can be created.

The idea of transferring a loop from one needle to another is the basis of the production of fully fashioned articles. By moving the loops from the outer needles inwards the width of the fabric is decreased, and by transferring loops outwards the width is increased. This method of manufacture will, however, be discussed in greater detail later in this chapter.

Warp-Knitted Fabric Constructions

In their simplest form weft-knitted fabrics can be produced from a single thread that makes rows of loops across the fabric. Warp-knitted structures on the other hand require a number of threads, each yarn producing a row of loops along the length of the material. The fabric is formed by the threads being moved from one needle to another on successive courses.

In warp knitting it is necessary to have guides to move the threads to the correct needle each time and also to pass the yarns around the needles. The movement of the guide to another needle is called an underlap and that around the needle which is the start of making a new loop is called an overlap.

Warp-knitted Tricot The simplest warp-knitted structure is a half-tricot, although this is of little commercial importance. There is one warp thread for every needle in the machine and at every course the warp threads are lapped round the needles and a set of loops is produced. The half-tricot is a 1 × 1 warp-knitted structure, where the underlaps are across only one needle. However, in this fabric the wales tend to be inclined at an angle (Fig. 7.1(b)).

Straight wales are produced by using two threads around each needle. Two 1 × 1 laps are formed in opposing directions and this results in a double fabric, called a tricot, which is not completely ladderproof (Fig. 7.7).

Warp-knitted Locknit Locknit fabrics are made with one needle bar but two guide bars, and by having two threads to every needle. The back guide bar laps over one needle in alternate directions, and the front guide bar laps in the opposite direction over two needles. The structure of this somewhat complex knitting is best illustrated by a diagram. Locknit is probably the most widely used warp-knitted fabric, because it has the advantage of not laddering easily and has a smooth surface (Fig. 7.8).

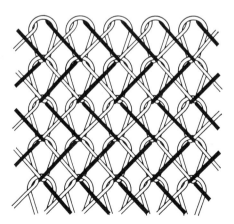

Fig. 7.7   Warp-knitted tricot (By courtesy of Columbine Press – Figures 7.7–7.10 are reproduced from Warp Knitting Technology by D. F. Paling, published by Columbine Press, Buxton)

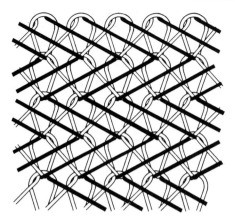

Fig. 7.8   Warp-knitted locknit

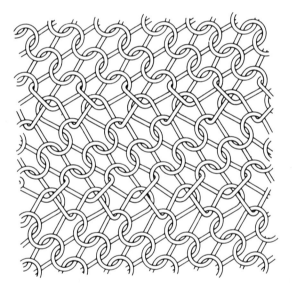

Fig. 7.9   Single atlas structure

Single Atlas   In this simple warp-knitted structure the threads are lapped in the same direction for a number of courses, and the direction is then reversed for a further number of courses. This sideways action produces zigzag stripes down the fabric. An atlas fabric is one of the warp-knitted structures that will ladder easily (Fig. 7.9).

Warp-knitted Net   Openwork fabrics which resemble lace can also be produced on warp-knitting machines by using suitable lapping movements in conjunction with partly threaded guide bars (Fig. 7.10).

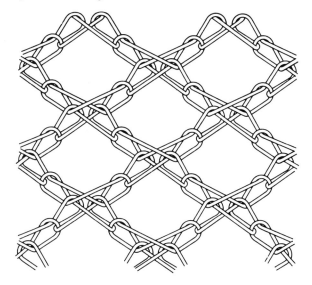

Fig. 7.10   Warp-knitted net with diamond-shaped openings

THE BASIC MECHANISMS OF KNITTING AND THE MACHINES USED

There are many different types of machines used in the knitting industry but these can be considered under the following broad headings:

(a) *Weft-knitting machines.* (i) Straight-bar machines, (ii) circular machines, (iii) flat-bar machines.

(b) *Warp-knitting machines.*

All these machines use needles of one kind or another, and there is one needle for each row of loops down the fabric.

The Needles   Several different types of needle are used on knitting-machines, including latch needles, bearded needles and compound needles. These are so designed that the thread can be held in the hook at the top of the needle but can also be released when necessary. There is one needle for every wale.

(a) The Latch Needle   This needle has a hook at the top, and the space between the hook and the stem of the needle can be bridged by a latch. The latch can swing freely as shown in Fig. 7.11. When it is closed the loop of yarn is held in the hook and as the needle moves upwards this existing loop opens the latch.

Fig. 7.11   A latch needle

In the position shown below in Fig. 7.12 no. 1 the needle is high enough to receive new yarn. The old loop is not cleared but remains across the latch and thus holds it down and prevents it from closing. The hook of the needle catches fresh yarn, which is fed from the guide bars. The needle is then raised so that the old loop is below the latch and the new yarn is in the needle hook. The needle is moved to its lowest position and the new loop is drawn through the old loop. As the needle moves downwards the old loop will move up the needle shaft and eventually slip off the needle, having closed the latch in the process. The new loop is held in the hook of the needle. The complete sequence can then begin again and the next course knitted (Fig. 7.12).

(b) The Bearded Needle   This needle is sometimes called a spring needle, and is again hooked but the top curved part continues down and finishes with a point (Fig. 7.13). This section is called the beard, and the needle is closed by pressing the point of the beard into a groove on the needle. The loop of yarn can be held in the hook at the top of the needle. When the needle bar moves downwards it will draw this loop through the previously formed stitches.

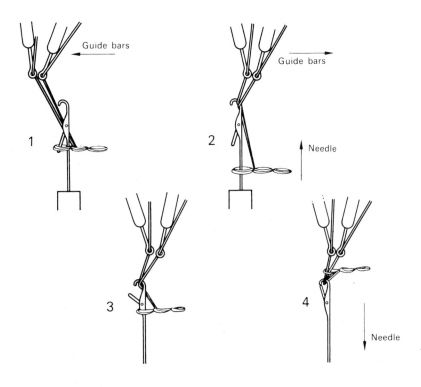

Fig. 7.12   Knitting action

Fig. 7.13   A spring or bearded needle

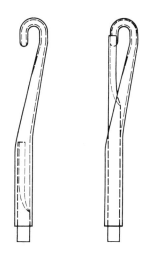

Fig. 7.14   A compound needle

(c) The Compound Needle   Latch and bearded needles have been found to be unsatisfactory for operation at high speeds on some of the newer machines, and the compound needle has been developed (Fig. 7.14). The main part of a compound needle is made from fine tubular steel with a hook at one end. A tongue is inserted in the tubular stem of the needle, and by vertical movement, this will open and close the needle hook.

The needles are set out in varying ways in the different machines.

Weft-knitting Machines

Straight-bar Machine – Including the Production of Fully Fashioned Garments

In these machines the needles are fixed in a straight bar as the name suggests and the loops are formed one after another on the needles. The straight bar moves vertically and one complete row of loops is brought through the row of old loops. This type of machine is used to knit a varied selection of merchandise including knitted outerwear and underwear in plain and rib, and stockings. This system is of particular value because it can be used to knit garment sections of a specific shape, an operation known as fashioning. The end loops can be moved outwards on to different needles and thus the width of the knitting is increased. Alternatively loops can be moved inwards on to needles already being used so that the fabric is narrowed. These preformed shapes can then be sewn up to form the garment. This method is used to produce high-quality, fully fashioned garments in which there is no waste from cutting. A full-fashioned machine has several sections, all sections producing panels of the same shape simultaneously. A set of fronts may be produced followed by backs and then two sets of sleeves, thus giving the panels for complete garments.

Circular and Flat-bar Machines – Including the Production of Cut and Stitch-shaped Garments

The appearance of the fashioned goods, as produced mainly on the straight-bar machines, is superior although the speed of production is comparatively slow. An alternative method of making a garment is by the 'cut and sew' principle. The knitted fabric is produced, and the required shapes are then cut out and sewn together. The fabrics are made on circular, flat-bar or warp-knitting machines.

Stitch-shaped garments are usually made with the rib knitted on the same machine. It is possible to control the machine to produce a welt, a rib and to change to a wider fabric. These products can be thought of as lying half-way between yard goods and fashioned goods. A certain amount of cutting is always required before the garments can be made up. Garments can also be cut out completely from flat or tubular fabric, as piece goods, and are used in underwear and outerwear, when a rib is not necessary.

Circular Machine   The diameter of these machines can vary considerably. Small cylinders of a few centimetres in diameter are used for knitting socks and stockings, but machines for producing outerwear and underwear vary from 30 to 80 cm in diameter. Since the needles are arranged in a circle the knitted material produced will obviously be tubular, and is drawn downwards through the centre of the machine (Fig. 7.15).

For the production of knitted piece-goods the fabric is cut, opened out and sold flat, and this forms the greater part of the material produced on circular knitting-machines. It is, in this case, of constant width throughout. However, it is possible to effect a certain amount of shaping, although fully fashioned articles cannot be produced on circular machines. Automatic circular knitting-machines can be used to produce a string of hose, which can then be separated and completed on another machine. The ribbed top, the plain section of the leg and the shaping for the heel can be produced automatically.

Recent developments include the use of sophisticated electronic patterning devices on circular knitting-machines to produce Jacquard jersey fabrics. Mini-computers are used for designing the patterns for the double jersey machines.

Flat-bar Machine   The particular feature of these machines is the wide variation of patterning that can be created, including Jacquard colour designs, although the production of fabric is rather slow. The domestic knitting-machine is of the flat-bar type suitable for being operated by hand. The flat-bar machine consists of two flat plates, called needle beds. These carry the two sets of needles and are mounted at right angles to each other. The knitted fabric passes downwards through the space between the two beds.

A number of automatic flat-bar machines have been designed to produce fashioned articles, a new development for this type of machine.

Fig. 7.15   Circular weft-knitting machine

Warp-knitting Machines

In warp-knitting machines the needles are fixed in straight bars, each needle being supplied with yarn from the warps by guides fixed in the guide bars. The great distinguishing point of warp-knitted fabrics is the fact that the threads run lengthwise (Fig. 7.16).

Warp-knitting machines can be used to produce fabrics suitable for shirts, lingerie and dresses; with modification to the threading of the guides and to the guide motions, openwork fabrics for lace, net and curtain net may be manufactured. The speed of production is comparatively high and warp knitting is still

Fig. 7.16   Warp-knitting machine

the fastest means of converting filament yarn into a conventional fabric of interlaced yarns.

The Raschel warp-knitting machine is used to produce fancy fabrics and many interesting and attractively patterned materials of this type are now available.

The new weft-insertion machine is basically a warp-knitting machine but has the ability to insert a weft yarn across the width of the machine, without a very large decrease in speed. Thus fabrics with a high degree of weftways stability may be produced for shirts, sheets etc.

Recent advances have included the development of the double-plush machine, which produces two plush fabrics face to face. These are then cut as a separate operation on another machine. Double-terry machines produce double-sided terry fabrics which, as the name implies, have loops on both sides of the material.

Photographs illustrating typical fabric types

A typical woven tweed fabric produced from woollen spun yarns. This is a coarse, heavy-weight rough surfaced fabric in which yarns of varying colours have been woven to produce a pattern

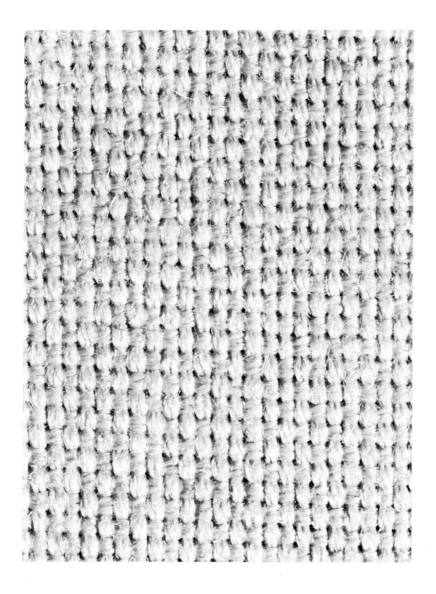

A hopsack fabric woven from spun yarns. The fibre ends can be seen projecting from the spun yarns, giving the fabric a 'hairy' surface. The weave is a modification of the plain weave known as a hopsack, in which two (or more) ends and picks have been woven as one

A moss crêpe fabric woven from continuous filament yarns. The photograph shows the 'smoothness' of these yarns in comparison with the 'hairiness' of spun yarns (compare the previous photograph)

A plain weave fabric made from Tricel-Fibro spun yarns. Mixture yarns of this type can be made from fibres of two or more colours blended together

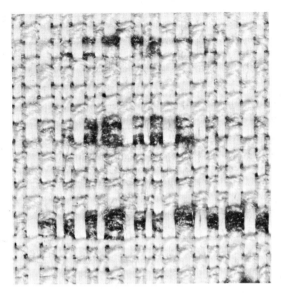

A fancy-weave fabric illustrating random picking. A smooth continuous filament yarn has been used to form the warp, and a spun yarn in a blend of Tricel and Fibro for the weft. The fabric has been cross-dyed and only the Fibro in the weft has been coloured black

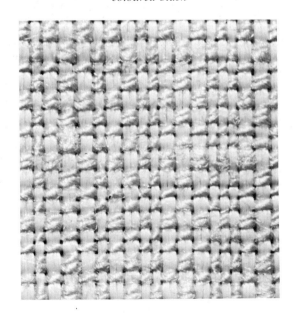

The same fancy-weave fabric as shown above with a filament warp and a spun weft in a blend of Tricel and Fibro. The fabric has, in this case, been plain-dyed

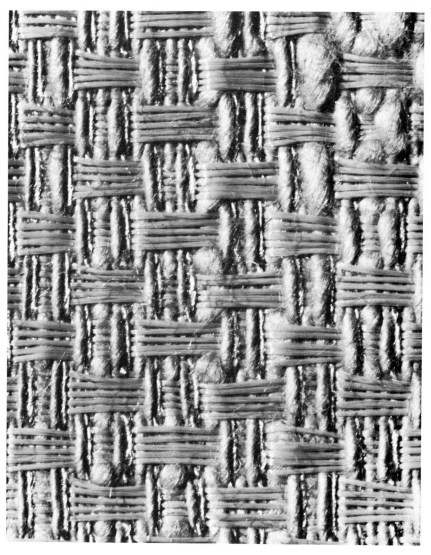

A fancy basket-type weave

A fabric woven from continuous filament yarns. The photograph illustrates the coloration of textiles by printing a design on the surface. This fabric has been roller printed

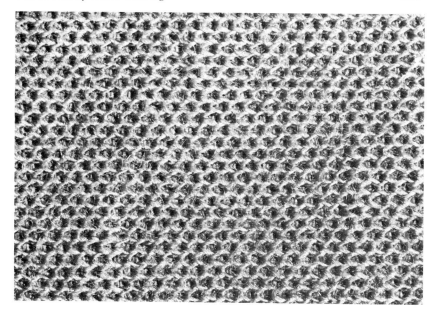

A knitted double-piqué fabric

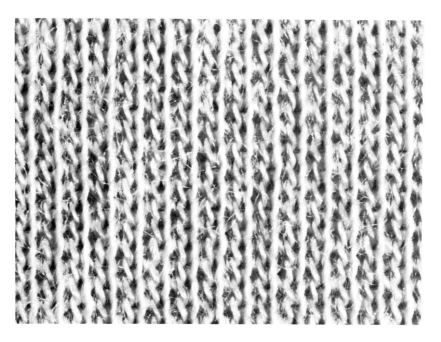

A doubleknit jersey fabric produced from an acrylic yarn

8. Fabrics Produced by Unconventional Methods

THE more conventional methods of producing fabrics by weaving or knitting have been in use for a long time, but the desire to make cloth by quicker and cheaper methods has led to the development of new techniques to produce non-woven fabrics.

In the absence of any better word being available in present terminology, 'non-woven' is used in this book as a generic term to cover the current methods of fabric production, other than the conventional methods of weaving and knitting, although it must be recognized that this is by no means an ideal expression. Until recently the term non-woven to most people implied bonded-fibre fabrics.

One technique consists of bonding the fibres together with an adhesive, others are based in general on stitching or needling and a fourth method develops spun-bonded non-wovens from filament yarns. The varying techniques may be summarized as follows:

(1) Bonded-fibre fabrics – adhesive bonding of fibrous webs.
(2) Needle-bonded fabrics – in which two or more webs of fibres are needled together, e.g. Fiberwoven.
(3) Stitch-bonded fabrics (a) in which warp and weft yarns are stitched, e.g. Malimo, (b) in which a web of fibres is stitched, e.g. Arachne, Maliwatt. Variations of this method include: Araloop – stitch-bonded fleece or scrim with pile; Malivlies – stitch-bonded, fibre-stitched; Malipol – stitch-bonded pile to scrim, and (c) in which 2 slit films at right angles are stitched, e.g. Malifol.
(4) Spun-bound fabrics – the manufacture of fibrous structures of synthetic polymers integrated with the production of the fibres themselves.
(5) Spun-laced – the manufacture of fibrous structures integrated by use of fluid jets.

All these techniques are potentially of great importance because they are less labour intensive and offer higher production speeds then conventional weaving or knitting. However, the fabric construction is at present limited, although this is in no way impeding progress in a number of end-uses. Bonded-fibre fabrics, as discussed later, have a wide range of applications. In the foreseeable future non-woven fabrics, aided by increasing technological advances, could well begin to make significant inroads into the markets at present held by more conventional textiles.

ADHESIVE BONDING OF FIBROUS WEBS

The principle involves the binding together of individual fibres to give sheet-like fabrics which are fairly strong and yet have some flexibility with good crease resistance. In the manufacture of bonded fibre fabrics there are basically three processing stages:

(1) Web formation.
(2) Application of bonding agent.
(3) Finishing process.

The method of production of a basic web of fibres is very critical, and if the basic web is of poor quality further processing will not correct this. After web formation the methods of bonding or finishing are numerous, but since most random webs have little or no strength they must be passed directly into the bonding process for best results. The web is fed into a bath where it is impregnated with adhesive or binder and thence into a drying-oven. The adhesive hardens on drying and holds the fibres together. Thermoplastic fibres can be used to make a web and, when they are heated, the fibres soften and stick together. Alternatively a percentage of thermoplastic fibre may be mixed with non-thermoplastic fibres, or thermoplastic fibres may be sprayed on to a web before the heat treatment.

Bonded-fibre fabrics are making considerable progress in end-uses such as interlinings, sold under such trade marks as Solena (Bonded Fibre Fabric Ltd) and Vilene (Bondina (Sales) Ltd). The interlinings can be used in all the places where previously scrim, cotton or linen interlinings and wool or hair canvas were used, for example jacket lapels, the front of raincoats or as an underskirt in a dress. They can also be used in conjunction with these materials.

The greatest advantages of bonded-fabric interlinings over conventional inter-linings are the good crease recovery and shape retention. They can also be very light and are thus ideal for use with the light-weight suiting fabrics now becoming very popular. These interlinings can be washed and dry-cleaned and are economical to use, since they can be cut in any direction without fraying. Due to the absence of warp and weft and the fact that there is no bias or selvedge, the pattern pieces can be laid in any direction, resulting in large fabric savings.

In the case of home-dressmaking, as the advantages become realized and now that the availability is increased, bonded-fibre fabric interlinings will be used more and more, as a simpler method of obtaining the desired shape, which will be retained.

Other end-uses are numerous and varied, including stiffeners, filter cloths, backing for coated fabrics, thermal insulation fabrics, wall coverings and shoe interlinings. The field of semi-durables covers such items as polishing and wiping cloths and table-cloths.

Owing to the economic prices of bonded-fibre fabrics they are used in dispos-able products, which are intended to be used once or perhaps a few times and then discarded – babies' nappy covers and liners, milk filters, clinical sheets and many medical uses, including surgical dressings and dental napkins. It is possible to supply, in disposable form, most of the textile requirements of a new baby, including gowns and bibs, nappies, sheets and pillow covers. The garments are used for a given time and when outgrown and stained they can be thrown away.

Some of the adhesive-bonded fabrics lack flexibility and complete textile-like drape, but recent bonded-fibre fabrics have become more sophisticated, and flexibility improved in some instances. Disposable fashion garments have been available in the United Kingdom and most of these have been sold through boutique-type establishments and have been successful mainly because of the bright, expensive prints which are applied. Of the two most successful bonded-fibre fabrics one has been based on viscose and the other on synthetic fibre, some having the added advantage of limited washability. The dresses from the synthetic fibre fabrics tend to be too expensive to be considered as completely disposable and some washability is therefore necessary as a selling aid.

The most important aspect still appears to be the cost of the garments. The fabric cost is now at an acceptable level and the printing cost is approximately the same, but making-up costs are still too high because of the labour involved. The labour costs account for some 50 per cent of the garment wholesale price. If these garments could be automatically laid up, die-cut and then seam-welded, the retail price of the garments could be reduced considerably. However, this awaits the time when manufacturers have the necessary techniques and machinery available. Much work is still to be done on the technique of welding, as this still tends to give somewhat stiffer seams than those produced by traditional stitch-seaming, which allows some movement.

In view of the very limited success of disposable fabrics in the fashion trade, the majority of manufacturers are turning more attention to the disposable overall and more utilitarian end-uses, including ladies' and children's briefs, sheets, pillowcases and towels and also surgeons' gowns.

New materials, which are in many ways similar to, though not a replacement for, leather have been tried. One such product was Corfam, produced by du Pont Ltd, but commercial production of this material has ceased at present.

These materials are outstandingly scuff-resistant and are cleaned rapidly by wiping with a damp cloth. Shoes made from these materials are comfortable to wear due to the softness of the fabric which conforms quickly to the shape of the foot and releases moisture.

THE PRODUCTION, PROPERTIES AND USES OF NEEDLE-BONDED FABRICS

Needling techniques are not new but the new machines have certain refinements, such as angled needles in the Chatham machine, on which the Fiberwoven blankets of Chas. Early and Marriott (Witney) Ltd are made.

In conventional cloth manufacture the fibres are arranged by spinning and weaving as already described. In the Fiberwoven process, however, the fibres are arranged and orientated by means of fine barbed needles.

The general needle-punch process consists of passing a matt or batt of fibres under, or between, barbed needles which quickly pass up and down through the batts locking the fibres together. The unique feature of the Fiberwoven process is the manner in which parts of the co-operating and oppositely disposed barbed

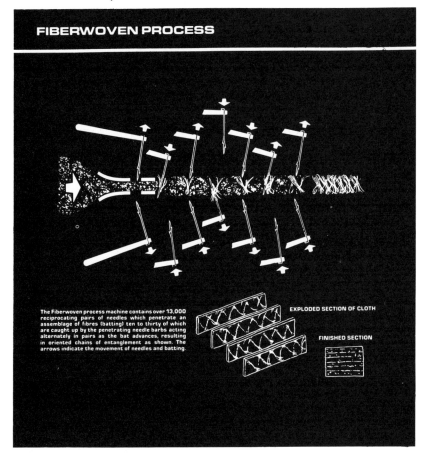

FIBERWOVEN PROCESS

The Fiberwoven process machine contains over 13,000 reciprocating pairs of needles which penetrate an assemblage of fibres (batting) ten to thirty of which are caught up by the penetrating needle barbs acting alternately in pairs as the bat advances, resulting in oriented chains of entanglement as shown. The arrows indicate the movement of needles and batting.

EXPLODED SECTION OF CLOTH

FINISHED SECTION

Fig. 8.1 · The Fiberwoven process

needles penetrate a batt alternately and in so doing pull or mesh the fibres into a chain of entanglement. Two layers of needles are involved and these penetrate the batts from both sides at angles (Fig. 8.1).

The needle-punch process for producing non-woven fabrics has great advantages because of the considerably lower cost compared with other textile production methods and blankets produced in this way combine the properties of warmth and strength.

More than 50 per cent of all blankets made in Britain and the U.S.A. are now produced by needle-punching. Care must be taken to ensure that the strength of these fabrics is adequate for the end-use for which they are intended, in this case blankets, and this is established by choosing fibre of the correct dimensions. Applications of needle-punched materials include, in addition to blankets, floor coverings, shoe and slipper linings and display fabrics.

The fibres normally used for the production of these fabrics are acrylics and polyesters, with a minority of viscose staple.

THE PRODUCTION, PROPERTIES AND USES OF STITCH-BONDED FABRICS

A third method of bonding together fibrous webs is by the use of stitching yarns knitted through the web with an action which is somewhat similar to that employed on conventional warp-knitting machines. Alternatively, crosslaid yarns may be stitched together.

Methods based on stitch bonding have developed principally from machines of the Mali type, an East German development, and Czechoslovakian machines including the Arachne type. Other machines include the ACHV and the British Kraftomatic. There are many different machine variations but Table 8.1 indicates those which are used for a given method of fabric production.

TABLE 8.1   DIFFERENT MACHINES USED FOR STITCH BONDING

Machine type	East German machines (Mali-)	Czechoslovakian machines (Ara-)	Russian machines	Other machines
Web stitching with thread	Maliwatt	Arachne	ACHV	–
Web stitching without thread	Malivlies Voltex	Arabeva	–	–
Pile stitching	Malipol	Araloop	ACHV	Kraftamatic Pickering Locstitch
Stitch-bonded fabric from 100 per cent yarn	Malimo	–	–	–
Slit-film stitching with thread	Malifol	–	–	–

It can therefore be seen that many variations are possible but it is proposed here to deal only with the basic principles of the methods of producing stitch-bonded fabrics, from a web by stitching with a thread, and from 100 per cent yarn.

The East German Mali machines began with the Malimo machine. For this system a warp is fed through the machine; a series of weft threads are laid across it and the warp and weft are stitched together using a third thread. The warp is taken from a beam and the weft threads from magazine creels at both sides of the machine.

The stitch-bonding of fibrous webs is carried out on the Maliwatt and Arachne machines. The Russian ACHV machine is only used in Eastern Europe. All three are fundamentally similar, except for needle design, and they basically warp-knit the stitching yarn through the fibre web. A range of fabrics can be produced with properties and characteristics which depend on the type of fibre in the web, the weight of the web, stitch density, machine needle gauge and type of stitching thread (Figs. 8.2, 8.3 and 8.4).

The most obvious advantages of these new methods of fabric production are in the reduction of the yarn cost and the fast operating speeds. Dependent on the web weight, productivity, assuming minimum courses per centimetre, can reach such remarkable values as up to 320 running metres per hour. Commercial fabrics are generally produced at 50–150 metres per hour.

Both the East German Malipol machine and the Czechoslovakian Araloop machine have been developed to manufacture pile fabrics. Both are capable of producing a pile on an existing fabric which may be a fleece, conventionally woven, knitted or may be a bonded fabric.

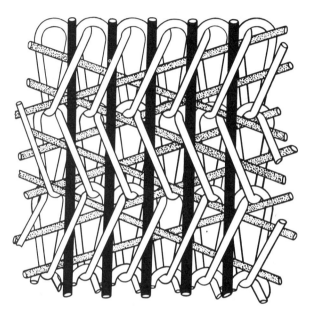

Fig. 8.2   Malimo fabric construction warp ■■ *weft* ▓▓ *stitching thread* ⬚

The Malipol machine has found application in the production of woollen blankets on a viscose backing fabric, and in the production of imitation fur acrylic fabrics, terry fabrics for beach wear and bathrobes, terry sheets and duvet covers.

The types of fabric produced from any one of these machines cut across the conventional categories of cloth manufacture in that they are not confined to one end-use, such as woollens, upholstery or menswear. Rather the machines are capable of manufacturing a limited number of cloths for a variety of end-uses.

Web Stitching with Thread

The basic machines Maliwatt and Arachne are confined to plain cloths which can be dyed and then finished to achieve a number of effects. Any variation of appearance is, therefore, obtained from blending fibres, dyeing and finishing (any one or all three). It should be added that surface effects can also be obtained by the use of different stitch types, but this is limited. The stitching yarn is, therefore, principally used as the structural binder of the cloth. Today one associates the basic machine with plain cloths but the variety of finishes which can be applied, by new and traditional finishing techniques, gives to these cloths remarkably interesting and delightful surface appearances. By choice of fibre and finishing, fabrics can be produced which are indistinguishable in appearance from some woven or knitted cloths. Alternatively, by different treatments quite new appearances can be achieved – all from what is actually the same basic structure.

Some of the end-uses that are well developed are listed opposite. The fabrics are widely available in the shops, but are not always recognized by the customer as being of this type. In some end-uses, such as curtains and mattress covers, they account for half the U.K. consumption, and they are now finding universal acceptance.

It is emphasized that these cloths will not necessarily replace the more traditional fabrics in a particular end-use but they will certainly enlarge the choice available.

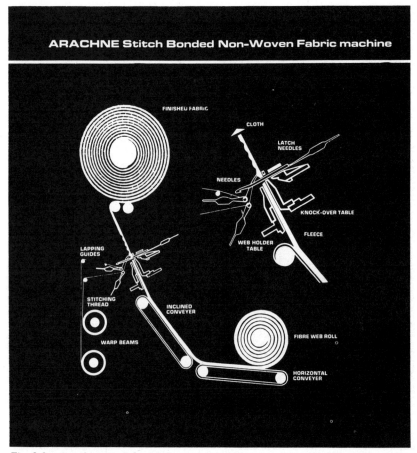

ARACHNE Stitch Bonded Non-Woven Fabric machine

Fig. 8.3   Arachne stitch-bonded non-woven fabric machine. Web from fibre roll is fed by inclined conveyor to latch needles, where stitching is inserted

Functional end-uses: Shoe and slipper components
Filter cloths
Backing fabric for PVC coating
Industrial cloths
Luggage and sports goods
Spectacle cases

Apparel end-uses: Dressing-gowns
Tie linings
Interlinings

Household end-uses: Bedspreads
Cushions
Mattress covers
Table-cloths
Wall coverings
Platform cloths in furniture manufacture

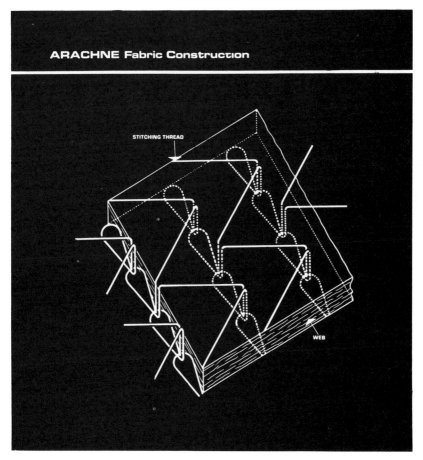

Fig. 8.4   Arachne fabric construction

The physical properties of the cloths produced by stitching a basic web must at least be comparable to those produced on orthodox machinery if they are to be acceptable. Their tensile strength can be twice that of woven goods and their slight increase in thickness usually means more warmth. It should be noted that the physical properties depend upon the type of fibre used as much as on the structure peculiar to the particular non-woven machine. On the basic machines almost every type of fibre from man-made and natural material can be processed, the fibre chosen being the one most suitable for the particular end-use.

It is expected that the technology of stitch-bonding will grow considerably, and therefore provide fabric appearances which cannot be imagined today, since already means of patterning are emerging.

Web Stitching without Thread

Web stitching without thread has end-uses which are mainly functional. This method can produce interlinings, waddings, and insulation materials. The absence of thread causes a loss in strength, but stability can be maintained by after-treatment. These products have applications as bonded linings in garments, or as industrial cloths.

Pile Stitching

Cloths from these machines mentioned in the table produce loop-pile fabrics on one side with the exception of the Kraftamatic process which produces a double-sided loop pile or terry cloth. Applications of these cloths exist in upholstery end-uses, towelling, bedding and beach wear. Pile heights can be adjusted to suit the end-use and the loop pile can also be removed by raising to give an interesting effect. The properties will be as good as existing terry cloths provided the raw materials are suitably chosen.

Stitch-bonded from 100 per cent Yarn

The Malimo method has already produced many extremely pleasant and interesting fabrics whose physical properties are good. It is easier to obtain a sheer cloth by stitch-bonding from 100 per cent yarn than by stitching a web with a thread, and lighter weights are more easily produced. Some of the end-uses include dress and blouse fabrics, ladies' suitings, shirtings, household curtainings and functional cloths. These fabrics have a good drape and handle with an interesting appearance.

SPUN-BONDED FABRICS

While other companies have been seeking to develop non-woven fabrics from staple fibres, du Pont have been working on the creation of a completely new class of textile materials called spun-bonded products; examples of this type of non-woven fabric are Reemay, a du Pont polyester product and Tyvek, also a polyester.

Spun-bonded products can be made in the form of sheets, tapes and laminates. Photomicrographs of these structures reveal that they are fine webs of randomly arranged, continuous filaments. The use of continuous filaments is one of the important features in this new material and gives it higher tear and tensile strengths. The random arrangement gives the structure approximately the same properties in all directions. The filaments are bonded together at crossover points and these bonds hold the fibres together in a sheet-like structure.

The filaments are continuously extruded on to a moving belt, being air-drawn through an aspirator. The filaments are electrically charged just below the aspirator, causing the individual filaments to separate. The fibrous web may then be bonded by various techniques ranging from adhesive bonding to the use of low-melting-point materials for thermal bonding.

Light-weight spun-bonded fabrics are used for interlinings, whereas the heavier structures of the spun-bonded polyester may be used as substrates in a number of coating and laminating applications, including bookbinding, wall coverings and backed leather.

One of the most interesting consequences of the introduction of these 'unconventional' methods of production may well be the fact that barriers will be broken down in what is at present a very sectionalized textile industry. Some people in the trade visualize fibre producers eventually carrying out all processes from start to finish. From the raw material the manufacturers could make the non-woven fabric and, with the use of die-cutting presses, cut to size and shape and perhaps weld together the finished garment. The methods are unlikely to replace normal weaving or knitting but as an addition to these they could make available a wider range of inexpensive clothes and also completely revolutionize our ideas on dress style.

9. The Processing of Textiles: Conversion of Grey Cloth

WHEN the material comes from the loom or knitting-machine it is not in a suitable state for immediate use, or for dyeing. There are natural impurities, such as waxes and lignin in cotton, fats and salts in wool, together with added substances such as size, oils and dirt picked up during processing. Before dyeing and finishing these are more or less completely removed.

Scouring aims at the uniform removal of waxes and fatty compounds so that the material can be 'wetted-out' ready for dyeing in aqueous solutions. Uneven removal of impurities can lead to faulty dyeing.

Other preparation treatments include desizing, to remove size from woven piece goods, singeing and mercerizing.

The fabric is then ready to be dyed, printed and finished by different techniques. Finishing in this context refers to processes which are carried out after dyeing, although the word is sometimes used to cover all processes which are carried out subsequent to weaving, including dyeing and printing.

The sequence of events in the processing of fabrics can be summarized as follows:

(1) *Purification and Preliminary Processing*
   Singeing
   Desizing
   Scouring and bleaching
   Fabric setting
   Mercerizing
(2) *Coloration*
   Dyeing at various stages, e.g. (i) stock dyeing, (ii) yarn dyeing, (iii) piece dyeing, (iv) garment or article dyeing
   Printing: (i) block-printing, (ii) screen-printing, (iii) roller-printing
(3) *Finishing*
   Mechanical
   Chemical

For any given fabric certain of these processes will be carried out, but the particular ones used and the methods employed will vary, depending on the cloth required. The different processes are now discussed in some detail. Much of the information refers to cotton and man-made fibres, but some indication of the variations in processing wool have been given.

PURIFICATION AND PRELIMINARY PROCESSING

Singeing

Fabrics are singed in order to produce a smooth surface (particularly important if the fabric is to be printed) and to minimize pilling of fabrics made from very strong staple fibres. The grey cloth has fibres projecting from the surface, giving a hairy appearance. These are removed by burning them away and two different types of machine are in use. Gas-singeing is now the most important method, where the flames from gas burners singe away the projecting fibres. The plate-singe consists of a curved surface of copper which is heated until it is red-hot, and the fabric is passed rapidly over this. Plate-singeing is only used for all-cotton fabrics as it is unsuitable for use with thermoplastic fibres. After singeing, the fabric is passed into a tank of water to put out any sparks. Obviously this process will not be needed for continuous filament yarns, as there will be no fibres projecting from the surface.

Desizing

Size is applied to the warp to help the yarns withstand the tensions imposed on them during weaving, but it is preferable to remove these starch-, gum- or gelatine-type substances before scouring and bleaching. Gum, gelatine and modern synthetic sizes are all readily water-soluble but starch must be broken down to render it water-soluble. This is usually done by enzyme treatment, but steeping in acid or treatment with an oxidizing agent may also be used.

Scouring and Bleaching

Scouring   In the case of cotton goods, scouring is usually carried out in large iron vessels called kiers (Fig. 9.1) and the fabric is treated with boiling alkali. The alkali forms soap with any free fatty acids and also splits the fats, a process known as saponification, giving soapy products. These can emulsify the oils and waxes and help keep the impurities suspended in the detergent solution.

The kiers are usually enclosed so that the cotton can be boiled under pressure in sodium hydroxide solution. This reduces the scouring time and means that the motes can also be removed. The motes are impurities such as particles of seed-coat and leaf, which are objectionable because they are coloured and difficult to remove or bleach. The exclusion of air from the kier helps to avoid the degradation of cellulose. In the presence of alkali and oxygen from the air, oxycellulose would be formed.

The cloth is laid and piled in rope form until the kier is full. The caustic soda solution is added to fill the vessel, and this is boiled to remove all air. The vessel is then closed and the solution circulated through the cloth using steam to both heat and pump it.

These methods are all batch processes in which a given quantity of fabric is

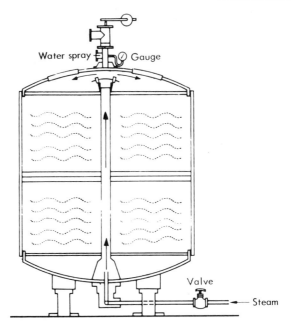

Fig. 9.1   A modern high-pressure kier

boiled with alkali and then rinsed. Newer continuous-processing methods can now be used.

Care must be taken in the purification of wool, since it is sensitive to the action of boiling water and hot alkaline solutions. Raw wool is scoured by moving it through warm detergent solution in baths. These are in sets of three to five, each bath having less detergent action than the previous one. Woollen and worsted pieces are scoured in rope form, often in a machine known as a dolly. Soda scouring is the normal process for woollen piece goods. Soap is formed by saponification of the wool fat.

Solvent extraction is now regularly used as an alternative to scouring, and can be combined with enzyme desizing.

Bleaching   The aim of the bleaching process is to obtain an evenly white fibre, yarn or fabric, and a good white is not necessarily associated with a high degree of purity in the material.

Bleaching agents can be either oxidizing agents or reducing agents. The reducing agents are generally only used to bleach the animal fibres, such as wool, although these can be bleached by oxidizing agents. Vegetable fibres are bleached with oxidizing agents.

The three most important bleaching agents in use today are sodium hypochlorite, often called 'chemic', hydrogen peroxide and sodium chlorite. The choice of agent depends on many factors such as the end-use of the fabric, the required handle and whether or not it is to be dyed. The various fibres require different bleaching agents and sometimes combinations of more than one chemical are used.

Cotton, being a vegetable fibre, will be bleached by oxidizing agents. These are usually either cold dilute solutions of sodium hypochlorite or hot dilute solutions of hydrogen peroxide.

Care has to be taken when treating materials with oxidizing agents because the fibres themselves are sensitive to attack. The problem is to allow the chemical to oxidize the colouring matter in the vegetable fibres and thus destroy these and give a good white colour, without attacking and degrading the cellulose to any extent. Bleaching must, therefore, be carefully controlled if damage to the fabric is to be avoided.

Overbleaching results in the secondary alcohol groups in the cellulose being oxidized to aldehyde groups or further oxidized to acidic groups.

$$\begin{array}{ccccc} \diagdown & & \diagdown & & \diagdown \\ CHOH & & CHO & & COOH \\ | & \rightarrow & & \rightarrow & \\ CHOH & & CHO & & COOH \\ \diagup & & \diagup & & \diagup \end{array}$$

Degradation of this type can be estimated by laboratory tests. The determination of the copper number indicates the number of reducing groups present, and is defined as the weight of copper reduced from the cupric to the cuprous state by 100 g of dry material. Methylene blue absorption is another way of estimating degradation and depends on the number of acidic groups present.

Degradation can also lead to chain breakage and hence the shorter molecules will have a lower molecular weight. The viscosity of a solution of cellulose in cuprammonium hydroxide solution will be altered, and this type of degradation can be estimated by fluidity measurements. Cellulose that has been partly hydrolysed or oxidized dissolves to give less viscous solutions at the same concentration.

Sodium hypochlorite in acid or neutral solutions would degrade the cellulose and give yellowing in storage. The reaction is, therefore, carried out under alkaline conditions. In alkaline solutions hypochlorites can be considered as oxidizing agents as follows:

$$NaOCl \quad \rightarrow \quad NaCl + (O) \qquad | \quad oxidation$$

The importance of careful bleaching during laundering cannot be overemphasized. Overbleaching will weaken the fabric considerably in the ways described above.

Hydrogen peroxide must also be used with alkali when bleaching cotton. Metal contamination must be avoided as this can lead to damage in hydrogen peroxide solutions due to catalytic action.

In the preliminary treatments continuous processes are now replacing the traditional batch methods. Open-width peroxide bleaching of cotton has largely replaced hypochlorite bleaching in a kier. The development of continuous combined desizing, scouring and bleaching units using trichloroethylene is at an advanced stage.

Wool is often sold in the natural, creamy colour obtained after scouring and many dyed woollens do not require bleaching. In contrast to cotton the amount of wool that is bleached is fairly small. One of the oldest ways of bleaching wool with a reducing agent is to expose the scoured material to sulphur dioxide gas. This

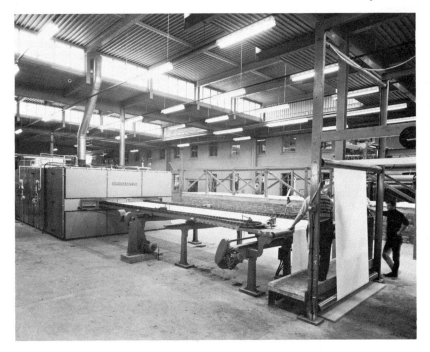

Fig. 9.2 Continuous bleaching and finishing (By courtesy of the Textile Council)

does not give a perfect white as with bleached cotton, and the effect is not permanent. On prolonged exposure to air the wool gradually reverts to the natural yellowy colour.

Wool can also be bleached by hydrogen peroxide, an oxidation process, but never with hypochlorite solutions. Chlorine damages the wool but can be used with care as an anti-shrink treatment.

In general, peroxide and chlorite bleaching are most suitable for regenerated cellulose fibres and for blends, and chlorite is suitable for synthetics.

Fluorescent whitening agents are universally used for all fibre types prior to printing, and in bleaching for whites.

Mercerizing

There are different opinions about the best time for mercerizing cotton. Some finishers feel that it should be carried out after bleaching, whereas others prefer to mercerize the cloth in the grey state.

The cotton is treated with alkali, usually sodium hydroxide solution, and this causes swelling of the fibre. Most cotton is mercerized under tension and the fabrics develop an attractive lustre and an increased affinity for dyestuffs. After treatment the alkali is removed by washing in water, and it is essential that all the alkali is washed out before the tension is relaxed, or the fabric will shrink.

The reasons for mercerizing are: (i) increased colour yield on dyeing/printing, (ii) improved easy-care properties, (iii) improved fibre lustre and (iv) more uniform dyeability.

Cotton fabrics can also be treated with sulphuric acid solution, and the finishes produced vary according to the concentration of the acid. Crêpe-like effects are obtained with the more dilute solutions and more concentrated acids give an effect referred to as parchmentizing. Parchmentizing causes stiffening of the fabric and linen-like effects can be produced. Care must be taken when treating cotton with sulphuric acid to make sure that the cellulose is not degraded by acid attack.

COLORATION

The Theory of Colour

Colour is often considered to be part of the object itself – a green tree, a blue sky and a red dress – although it is strictly a sensation produced when the eye, and related nervous system, is stimulated by radiant energy of certain wavelengths.

Light is a form of radiant energy, i.e. electromagnetic waves of medium wavelength. Figure 9.3 illustrates that the waves having very short wavelengths are called gamma rays and X-rays, and these exhibit varying degrees of penetration through material. The infra-red heat waves and radio waves have long wavelengths. Covering a relatively small section of the spectrum between the two is the visible spectrum, the wavelength for violet being the shortest and red the longest of the visible rays.

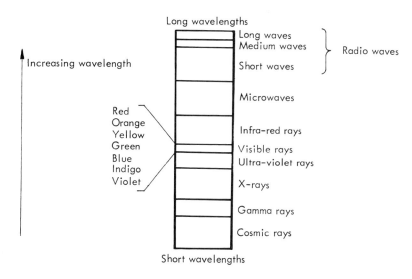

Fig. 9.3   The electromagnetic spectrum

Spectrum

If white light falls on an object it may be either reflected or absorbed, wholly or partially.

If all the light is absorbed then there will be no radiant energy reflected from the surface of the object, and it is referred to as a black body. On the other hand, certain materials reflect most of the light so that the rays of the visible spectrum are still in the correct proportions. These appear white. Other bodies are selective, certain wavelengths are reflected and the others are absorbed. The rays reflected will be the complement of the rays absorbed, and hence if red light is absorbed then green will be reflected. The colour of an object depends therefore on which wavelengths it absorbs and which it reflects, and to what extent.

A dye can be considered as a substance which can be fixed to a material and by the selective absorption of certain wavelengths will produce a sensation of colour. This colour depends mainly on the structure of the dye molecule.

A grouping within a molecule, which creates a sensation of colour, is referred to as a chromophore group. The chromophore group contains double bonds between atoms, and the dye molecules below indicate these conjugated double bonds – alternate single and double bonds between atoms.

Dyes

It is possible to produce coloured textiles in various ways, but true dyeing involves the penetration of the dye into the fibre, and the subsequent holding of

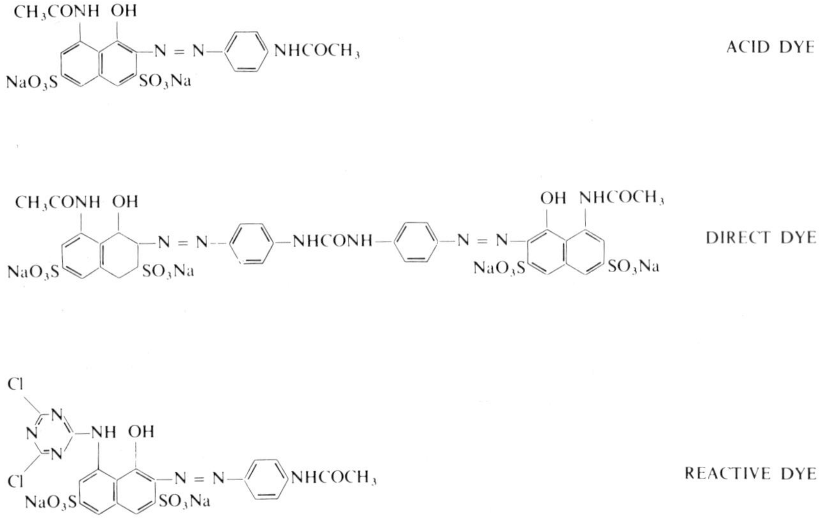

Fig. 9.4   Dye molecules

this dye within the fibre structure. The process can be carried out in a number of ways, the method of application and the way in which the dye is held within the fibre depending on the particular dye class and on the fibre composition.

The Basic Dyes   As the name suggests, these dyes are basic in character due to the presence of amino groups. They combine with acids and can therefore be used to dye wool, since this is a protein containing acidic groups. Basic dyes produce brilliant colours, but on wool they are not usually very fast to light, laundering or perspiration. A more important use nowadays is with the acrylic fibres which also contain acid sites and are normally dyed with these dyes. Many new basic dyes with extremely good fastness have been developed for this purpose.

In order to dye cellulosic materials with basic dyes a mordant is used. The mordant is first applied to the cotton fabric and the basic dye is then applied. The mordant reacts with the dye which is then held on to the material.

Acid Dyes   Acid dyes are applied in acid solution, and are usually sodium salts of sulphonic acid. The acid dye in Fig. 9.4 depends for its application properties on the two sodium sulphonate groups, which confer water solubility and anionic character. These dyes have an affinity for wool, as the acidic dye is attracted by the basic components of the protein molecule. They are also used extensively for nylon.

Metal Complex Dyes – There are several instances where metals can be used to form co-ordination complexes with dyes, to give important improvements in wash fastness. The chrome dyes have been important for wool for many years, and more recently premetallized acid dyes, in which a metal, usually chromium, is used, have become available. These are used on wool and nylon to give colours of good wash fastness and very good light fastness.

Direct Dyes   Direct cotton dyes are water-soluble compounds, also comprising sodium salts of sulphonic acids, but of larger molecular size than most acid dyes. They are relatively inexpensive and easy to apply. They are widely used on cotton and viscose fabrics and the dye molecules are absorbed on to the cellulose chain and held by hydrogen bonding and Van der Waals forces. The direct dyes on cotton are not held by polar groups as with acid dyes on wool. It is difficult to obtain a high degree of fastness to washing, but this can be improved by certain after-treatments, such as treatment with copper salts. The copper forms co-ordination compounds with the dye molecule.

The dyeing process can be extremely simple; as the name implies, the dye is applied directly from a hot aqueous dye solution, in the presence of common salts which are needed to regulate the rate of dyeing.

Disperse Dyes   The disperse dyes have no ionic groups and consequently are almost insoluble in water. They are 'hydrophobic' and can be regarded as able to 'dissolve' in the hydrophobic fibres in preference to water. The dyes are applied as a finely divided dispersion in the presence of a surface-active agent.

Disperse dyes were introduced in the first place for acetate, the first fibre to be developed that could not be dyed with the classes of dyes then available for the natural fibres. They are now widely used as well on triacetates, nylon, polyesters and acrylics and are potentially useful on any hydrophobic fibre. They are not used for hydrophilic fibres such as wool. The temperature at which they are applied depends on the fibre concerned. For example, acetate can be dyed at relatively low temperatures, whereas polyesters require to be dyed at temperatures above 100°C, i.e. under pressure, or in the presence of a carrier.

Vat Dyes   The vat dyes are insoluble in water, but by chemical reduction they are converted to the leuco form, which is soluble in alkali. In this reduced soluble form the vat dyes can be applied to cellulosic fibres, since under these conditions the dye has an affinity for the fibre. The dye is then reoxidized to the insoluble form on the material and the true colour develops.

The vat dyes can be extremely fast to washing and to light. Vat dyes are available in a wide range of colours, particularly blues and greens, but are deficient in reds and oranges.

Sulphur Dyes   Chemically these are similar to the vat dyes. They have to be solubilized with alkaline sodium sulphide, a reducing agent, then reoxidized after dyeing to the insoluble form. The shade range is limited and fastness is not as good as with vat dyes. However, since sulphur dyes are relatively inexpensive they are used for work wear.

Azoic Dyes   The azoic dyes are developed on the fibre by the combination of two components. Diazo compounds are produced when certain amines are treated with nitrous acid. The resulting diazonium salt, when coupled with a suitable naphthol, gives an insoluble compound which is highly coloured.

For cotton, the most important substrate, the fabric is first treated with the naphtholate and is then passed through the diazo solution. The dye is formed on the fabric and the colour develops. The azoic dyes give bright reds and yellows, but the range is deficient in blues and greens. Azoic dyes usually have good washing and light fastness.

Reactive Dyes   The reactives are a relatively new class of dye containing special groups, which enable the dye to react chemically with reactive groups on the fibre. In this way, a covalent bond is formed between the dye and the fibre; because of this bond very good washing fastness is obtainable.

Reactive dyes are available in a wide range of bright shades covering the whole of the spectrum, and with several types of reactive group which enable different application methods to be used.

Pigments   Pigments are naturally insoluble and are, therefore, not suitable for colouring textiles by conventional dyeing or printing techniques. They can, however, be fixed on to a fabric by using a resin to bond them to the surface of the fibre. Resin-bonded pigments can be applied by pad-dyeing or printing techniques to give unusual colour effects of surprisingly good fastness. They are important for colouring glass fibre fabrics. Mention is made later of the use of pigments in spin-dyeing.

Dyeing

Dyeing can take place at many different points during textile processing. The colourant can be added during fibre manufacture, a technique known as spin-dyeing, or the woven or knitted fabric can be dyed. The material can also be dyed at numerous stages between these two extremes, in different forms such as tow, loose fibre or yarn. In the case of knitwear the garment can be dyed.

The point at which dyeing is carried out depends on a number of considerations such as cost, flexibility of supply and the nature of the fabric or garment being produced. For example, colour-woven fabrics can only be obtained if dyeing is carried out prior to weaving. It is often convenient to dye loose fibre but this means that the shade is fixed at a very early stage in the manufacture of the final article. Certain knitwear can be dyed in garment form, which is convenient because the manufacturer does not have to make an early forecast about his colour requirements. His stock of garments or fabric can be held in the grey state and then fairly readily dyed when it is known what colour is required. This is particularly advantageous when colour is dependent on fashion and is thus difficult to predict. The manufacturer producing spun-dyed yarns has to decide which colour will be in demand some time in advance, but these colours can be very fast to light and washing.

THE DIFFERENT WAYS OF INTRODUCING COLOUR INTO TEXTILES

Spin-dyeing This technique is also referred to as dope-dyeing or mass pigmentation. The dye or pigment is incorporated in the molten polymer, or in a polymer solution and this is then extruded through the spinneret in the usual way. The coloured pigments will therefore be within the fibre, between the molecules. Bright, strong colours can be produced, and these are fast to light and washing.

Pad-dyeing The dye is made into a solution or suspension with a liquid which is usually water. This is then applied to the fabric uniformly and in a controlled amount. This method is widely used for cellulosic fibres and their blends, and when the dye has little affinity for the fabric.

The fabric is passed through the dye bath, which contains a constant and carefully calculated concentration of dye, and is then passed between the rollers of the pad mangle, to squeeze out the excess dye liquor. In order to ensure that the dye is evenly applied all over the fabric the pressure between the two rollers must be constant. The dye is 'fixed' by a heat treatment or steaming or, in the case of the azoics, by application of the second component, and then has to be well rinsed and/or soaped to remove any unfixed dye.

Exhaustion Dyeing The material is immersed in the dye liquor and the dye is absorbed by the fibre. An essential feature of this technique is that either the dye liquor or the fibre/fabric must be kept moving, otherwise uneven dyeing results. For loose fibre or tow in a perforated basket (Fig. 9.6) or for fabric on a perforated beam (Fig. 9.5), dye liquor is circulated through the fibre mass. Fabrics are more usually moved through the dye liquor. Even under good conditions for obtaining an even dyeing, time has to be allowed for 'levelling' and penetration of dye molecules into the fibre. Exhaustion dyeing can be used for soluble dyes which have an inherent affinity for the fibre, such as acid dyes for wool, and direct dyes for cotton. However, it can also be used to apply 'insoluble' disperse dyes from aqueous dispersion on to hydrophobic fibres. The rate at which the dye is taken up by the fabric depends on many factors, including the composition of the dye bath, its temperature and the liquor ratio, which is the ratio of the volume of the liquor to the amount of material.

MACHINES USED FOR DYEING

When yarn is dyed on packages the material is kept stationary and the liquor moves. Loose fibre, slivers and tops can be loaded into perforated containers through which the dye liquor is pumped (Fig. 9.6). Cheese-dyeing takes place by fitting the cheeses of yarn on to a perforated spindle and placing in a hollow cylinder. The dye liquor is circulated by pumping through the perforated spindles and yarn to give even coloration.

Fig. 9.5   Dyeing fabric on a beam. The fabric is loaded, having been previously wound on to a beam, into the machine

Alternatively the textile material can be moved through the dye liquor. Hanks of yarn used to be hung on wooden poles and moved across the dye bath, although the modern method is to circulate the dye liquor.

One method for dyeing piece goods that must not be creased is on a jig. There are two rollers above the dye bath and the fabric is wound from one roller and passed to the other through the liquor. The direction is then reversed and the fabric is wound back on to the first roller, again through the liquor. This is repeated until the required shade is obtained. This type of fabric can also be dyed on a perforated beam.

The winch machine is also used to dye fabric. The material is sewn to form a continuous band of fabric which is passed round and round, over the winch and through the liquor (Fig. 9.7).

Fig. 9.6   Dyeing tow – the tow is being loaded into the dyeing containers. A firm pack must be obtained before dyeing is commenced

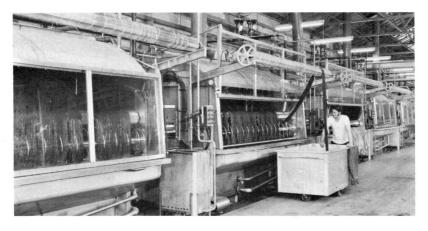

Fig. 9.7   The winch-dyeing of fabric

The pad mangle has already been discussed; it is simply a shallow trough and a pair of squeeze rollers.

Warp-knitted fabrics are frequently dyed on a perforated beam and the dye liquor circulated to give even coloration (Fig. 9.5). Jet-dyeing has been developed for weft-knitted fabrics. In these dyeing machines the fabric is transported mechanically by liquor jets.

Printing

Printing involves the application of dyes to the surface of the cloth usually in specific localized areas. The same types of dye are used in printing as in dyeing but there are special means of application. It is necessary to thicken the dye solution with materials such as starch, to give a thick paste, so that the colour can be applied in a given pattern and will not run and spread outside the limits of the pattern. The colour is then fixed on a printed fabric by steaming; this softens the paste and allows the colour to penetrate within the fibre.

There are three important methods of printing textiles by the wet process: block-, screen- and roller-printing. A more recently developed method is transfer-printing from a paper substrate, a dry process.

Block-printing   Printing with hand blocks is one of the oldest forms and is similar to using an ink-pad and stamp. The design is cut out in relief in a suitable type of wood. The colour is picked up on the block. This is taken to the fabric, and the colour is transferred from the block to the fabric. Every colour requires a separate block, and the pattern is matched each time by using pegs at the corners and edges of the blocks. Block-printing is still used to a limited extent for the decoration of scarves.

Screen-printing   Screen-printing can be considered as a form of stencilling. Originally silk was stretched over a wooden frame, but today other materials such as nylon and glass-fibre fabric can be used to make the screen. The design is applied to the screen; the areas where colour is required allow the colour paste to be pressed through the open meshes, whereas the remainder of the screen is blocked out.

The fabric to be printed is placed on a long table and the screens are placed accurately in position over the cloth. Coloured paste is poured on to the screen and forced through the mesh by squeezing. A screen will be required for each colour. The fabric moves along the table until each colour in the design has been applied, care being taken to ensure that the pattern is in register.

One method of applying the design is to treat the whole screen with light-sensitive gelatine. The pattern is formed by applying a light-resistant material to certain areas and then exposing the screen to light. This light causes the soluble gelatine to become insoluble where it is not protected. However, the protected areas will remain soluble and can be washed away, leaving the untreated gauze in the areas where colour is required, with the rest of the screen blocked out. Preparation of screens is relatively easy and not as expensive as the engraving of a roller for roller-printing, although the length of fabric which can be printed with one set of screens is less than with one roller (Fig. 9.8). Screen-making is, however, time-consuming.

Roller-printing   The design is engraved on a copper roller, each colour in the design having its own roller. The pattern is etched so that the sunken parts are the ·

Fig. 9.8   Screen-printing

areas where colour is required (Fig. 9.9). The engraved roller is rotated in the colour paste and the excess is removed by a blade. Colour only remains in the sunken parts and the roller is then pressed on to the cloth. The engraved rollers, one for each colour, are fixed around a large cylinder, over which the fabric to be printed passes. The printing rollers are driven and adjusted so that the patterns are in register. These printing rollers are in contact with the large cylinder and cause this to rotate (Fig. 9.10). The rollers can be engraved by hand, by machine or by chemical etching.

All printed fabric has to be dried and the colours must be fixed. The fabric is usually treated with steam and some pigments have to be oxidized. The fabric is then given a washing and rinsing treatment and dried.

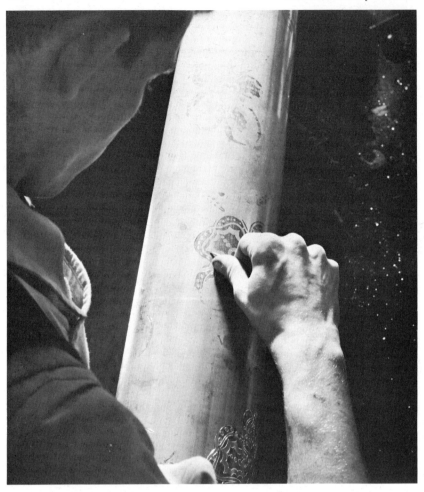

Fig. 9.9   Hand-engraving a copper roller for fabric printing

Discharge- and Resist-printing   The usual method of printing is to apply the colour as described above. This is 'direct' printing. It is also possible to discharge locally a colour applied by dyeing, by printing on a suitable chemical – discharge-printing.

Alternatively, chemicals can be printed on to a white fabric. These will prevent the treated areas from taking up colour in a subsequent dyeing operation – resist-printing.

Transfer-printing   This method is used for printing on polyester. It is a dry process in which disperse dyes, printed on specially prepared paper, are caused to vaporize by heating and so to transfer to fabric against which the transfer-paper is held on a cylinder.

Fig. 9.10 Roller-printing

FINISHING

Finishing processes are designed to improve the handle and appearance or sometimes the performance of the finished fabric. The finishing will not necessarily be carried out in the final stages of production. Fabric is mercerized or milled at a fairly early stage, but calendering and stentering are performed as final stages. The techniques used are wide and varied, but may conveniently be considered in sections according to whether the treatment is mechanical or chemical.

Mechanical and Physical Finishing

Adjustment of the dimensions of the fabric

> *Width and length.* Stentering, jigging.
> *Stable dimensions.* Heat-setting of thermoplastic fibres.
> *Thickness.* Increased by raising or sueding, reduced by calendering.

Handle or appearance

> *Non-permanent additives* including finishes to alter surface, waxy softeners, stiffeners such as starch. } Not wash-fast
> *Semi-permanent additives.* Increased lustre, smoothness or embossed appearance by calendering.

Stentering   Goods are adjusted to the required dimensions during the drying process and the creases are removed. This treatment is referred to as stentering (or tentering) and the equipment used is called a stenter (or tenter).

Stentering is necessary for all fabrics in order to straighten and set the fabric to the desired width and length. In the case of a clip stenter the fabric is fed into the machine and the sides of the fabric are held by clips, attached to a moving band. The distance between the travelling bands on each side gradually widens and is adjusted so that the material is stretched to a predetermined width.

The cross-rails of a clip stenter can be made to oscillate so that the fabric is subjected to a 'to-and-fro' motion, which helps to straighten the weft threads. This is called 'jigging'. The fabric is carried through the stenter and dried with hot air.

The pin stenter is based on the same principle, but the fabric is held at the sides by pins. This means that the fabric can be over-fed on to the pins, and thus fully relaxed fabrics can be produced (Fig. 9.11).

Calendering   Calendering corresponds to domestic ironing and smooths or flattens a fabric. A calender consists of a series of rollers, or bowls, which rotate in contact usually under high pressure, and can often be heated. The fabric is passed between the rollers. Friction calendering is the process of passing fabric through a

Fig. 9.11 The stenter. The stenter pulls the fabric to the precise width required and then sets it by heat at this width. This shows a pin stenter, where the fabric is held at its selvedges by a large number of pins

calender in which a polished heated steel roller revolves at a higher surface speed than a softer roller against which it works. A glaze is produced on the face of the fabric that is in contact with the steel roller.

The primary object of Schreiner calendering is to enhance fabric lustre. One of the rollers is a steel bowl engraved with very fine lines running at an angle of about 20° to the vertical or the horizontal. Embossing involves the use of more deeply engraved bowls (see below).

The Use of Additives The handle of a fabric can be improved by the use of additives. Starch can be added as a stiffening agent to give the fabric a crisp, full handle, although this effect will not be fast to washing. The starch may also contain softening materials or filling agents such as china clay, which give the fabric body and fullness.

Back-filling is the term used to describe the technique of pressing a thick starch paste into one side of the fabric. This fills the interstices and gives body to the fabric without affecting the face of the cloth.

Many other treatments can be given to fabrics to alter the appearance or properties in some way. It is not possible to discuss all these in this text and only the more important ones are mentioned below.

Beetling Beetling is a treatment given to linen to produce a flat effect and to give it lustre. The cloth is wound on to a revolving wooden roller and beaten by heavy wooden hammers, which soften the linen and flatten the yarns.

Raising Raising operations involve disentangling the fibre ends, and lifting them to the surface so as to give a lofty, 'woolly' handle. Cylinders of card-wire or teasles are used, and the pile can be made to either stand erect or lie in one direction. This operation is also referred to as gigging. A special machine may be used to rub the pile into a pattern, such as waves, a treatment known as rippling.

Milling Wool fibres are able to felt, whereby the fabric becomes thicker and denser as the fibres become matted together. This is aided by the presence of scales on the wool fibre. During milling the wool is subjected to moisture, heat and pressure. These cause the material to form a consolidated mass, and in heavily milled fabric the original weave may be obscured and the yarn structure broken down. Milling is usually used for wool and wool blends, although this is not exclusively the case.

Mercerizing Mercerizing involves the treatment of cotton fabrics with sodium hydroxide solution under tension, to improve the lustre and dye-affinity of the fabric. This has already been discussed earlier in the chapter but is included here for completeness.

Chlorination Chlorination can be used to reduce the felting properties of wool, and to improve its dimensional stability, especially making it less liable to shrink in washing. The wool is steeped in acidified sodium hypochlorite solution, and the chlorine liberated acts on the wool. Alternatively, chlorine gas can be used on dry wool. Chlorinated wool dyes more rapidly and feels slightly harsher than the untreated wool.

Softening Softeners are often required on fabrics such as dress goods and numerous preparations are available. These softeners are based on fatty substances such as oils and waxes.

Embossing A design is impressed on the fabric by passing it between two rollers. An engraved steel roller is used plus a cotton roller, which is dampened with soap and water. The steel roller is run against the cotton roller and the design is impressed into the cotton roller. The fabric, softened by heat or moisture, is passed between the two rollers, and the design is impressed into it. Thermoplastic materials are patterned by a design, which will be permanent at the normal temperatures of use and washing.

Heat-setting It has already been explained that many polymers such as nylons, polyesters, acrylics and the triacetates are thermoplastic. This means that they soften when subjected to sufficiently high temperatures but 'harden' again on cooling. Consequently, thermoplastic fibres can be heated and moulded to a new shape. This will be discussed in more detail when the properties of textiles are considered in Chapter 10, but this process can be used to produce permanent pleats and to obtain smocked effects. Since these effects have been heat-set into the fabric they will be permanent unless the material is subjected to temperatures similar to those used for heat-setting.

During its production a fabric is subjected to stretching and strain is imposed on the cloth. Unless this stretch is removed in finishing, the fabric will shrink during the first wash. With thermoplastic fibres the strain can be nullified by heat treatment, a process known as heat-setting. The fabric is subjected to a high temperature, usually much greater than the boiling-point of water, and on cooling the fabric is quite stable in the slightly stretched state and will not shrink during washing, unless the temperature reached is similar to that used to set the fabric.

In the case of cotton goods the 'relaxation shrinkage' can be removed by a treatment called compression shrinkage. 'Rigmel' or 'Sanforized' cotton fabrics are compression-shrunk.

Permanent Finishes Obtained by Chemical Treatments

Most of the older methods of finishing, such as treatment with glue, china clay, starch and chlorine, are relatively cheap and have been available for a long time. However, more recently, specific organic compounds have been developed, which, although more expensive, can be used to produce permanent effects such as drip-dry and non-iron fabrics, and for permanent-press finishes, moth-proofing, flame-proofing and rot-proofing. These synthetic resins are complex organic compounds of high molecular weight.

Crease-resistant Finishes Urea-formaldehyde and melamine-formaldehyde are widely used to produce crease-resistant cellulose or cellulose/synthetic blend fabrics. The handle of the treated fabric must not be spoilt and the finish must be fast to washing. For this reason, the resin is inside the fabric and not merely on the surface. The urea and formaldehyde are reacted together to give a urea-formaldehyde resin, and the fabric is then impregnated with a solution of this water-soluble resin. After drying to the required dimensions, the impregnated fabric is heated in order to 'cure' the resin. During the curing process the resin molecules already in the fabric polymerize and cross-link. The resin is then water-insoluble and permanently in the interior of the fibres. When the resin polymerizes it introduces cross-linkages between the long cellulose molecules. The fabric is washed in order to remove any uncombined products. This treatment gives the fabric a durable, crease-resistant finish, and since the resin is insoluble, this property will be retained after repeated washing.

Anti-shrink Treatments As a result of the standard crease-resistant process cotton and viscose materials also possess resistance to shrinkage, an added advantage in wear.

Another method of producing 'anti-shrink' materials is by the production of methylene cellulose. Viscose is treated with formaldehyde in the presence of an acid catalyst and methylene cellulose is formed. Cotton and viscose fabrics treated in this way do not shrink as much during normal laundering as untreated fabric, but unfortunately the goods are liable to be damaged during the treatment by acid attack.

Melamine-formaldehyde resins have been used on wool to make it 'shrink-proof'. They are, however, expensive. The normal methods of finishing wool to make it shrink resistant are based on pre-chlorination (see p. 154) often followed by coating with a substantive agent which will polymerise on drying.

Moth-proofing Permanently moth-proof fabrics are obtained by impregnating the fibres with non-volatile substances, which make the material unsuitable as food for the grubs of the moth. Any inorganic compound containing fluorine will give moth-proof properties to wool, and many synthetic organic compounds have also been developed as moth-proofing agents. The Dielmoth process depends on the impregnation of the fabric with Dieldrin, a complex mixture of chlorinated hydrocarbons. This process is cheap and effective, producing a finish that is fast to laundering and dry-cleaning. Due to its high toxicity to the grubs, Dieldrin gives complete protection to the fabric against attack by the clothes-moth.

Flame-proofing   One of the most successful durable flame-proofing processes so far developed is the Proban finish, which was produced by Albright and Wilson and the Bradford Dyers Association. The Proban finish depends on the application of THPC, a complex organic compound containing phosphorus and chlorine. This will react with ammonia to give an insoluble polymer. The material, impregnated with THPC, is treated with ammonia and a flame-proof finish is given to the fabric. The original finishes of this type stiffened the fabric, but the newer techniques produce fabrics with a more satisfactory handle that is not so harsh. Care is needed in laundering in order to avoid the accumulation of lime-soap deposits which impair the efficiency of the finish (p. 172).

Another organic phosphorus compound used to produce flame-retardant finishes on natural and regenerated cellulosic textiles is Pyrovatex CP, developed by Ciba-Geigy. The finish has good fastness to washing and dry-cleaning and the handle of treated fabrics is good.

Cheaper but less permanent methods of flame-proofing depend on the use of a solution of borax and boric acid, or alternatively an aqueous solution of ammonium phosphate and ammonium chloride.

Water-proofing   It is necessary to differentiate between waterproof and water-repellent or shower-proof fabrics. Waterproof fabric can be produced by treatment with a drying oil, which oxidizes to give a flexible coating. The first oilskins were produced by the application of several layers of linseed oil, each coating being allowed to dry before the next was applied. Linseed oil is still the chief finishing material for oiled skins. Fabrics for tarpaulins or canvas roofings are produced by impregnating heavy cotton fabric with hot mixtures of pitches and waxes.

Water-repellent finishes can be applied to produce fabric that is still air-porous. Aluminium compounds can be used alone, or with soap, when they are converted into an aluminium soap to give a water-repellent effect. Shower-proofing with wax is used on light-weight fabrics, the oils or waxes being applied from solution or from an aqueous emulsion.

When silicones are applied to fabrics, on curing, the polymer cross-links to give a complex structure of high molecular weight. Water-repellent fabrics can be developed by using material that reacts chemically on the fibre. One method is to treat cellulose with an acid chloride to produce cellulose esters. The surface compound is then hydrophobic and the finish permanent.

Fluorocarbon complexes can be used to give durable water-repellency. The Minnesota Mining and Manufacturing Company Ltd have patented a water-repellent finish under the registered trade mark of Scotchgard, based on fluorochemicals.

Bonding and Laminating   Two fabrics each with their own properties of handle and drape may be bonded or laminated together, either with an adhesive or with a thin layer of polyurethane foam. The resulting material will have characteristics different from the two component fabrics.

10. Properties – Fibres, Yarns and Fabrics

THE properties of a fabric depend on many factors in addition to the fibre properties. It is, therefore, impossible to generalize and state that a given fibre will produce a particular type of fabric. Fine denier filament nylon can be made into the lightest of sheer chiffons, which are very different from the heavy jersey fabrics produced from bulked nylon yarn. The finished fabric will depend on the way in which the yarn is produced and on the fabric structure. The properties may also be altered by the application of different types of dyes and finishes, which have been discussed in the previous chapter.

The diagram below illustrates the interrelationship of the various factors influencing fabric properties.

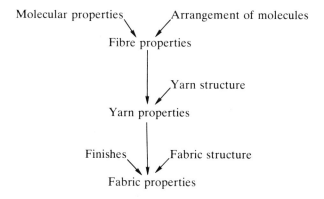

To the consumer the important considerations are the properties of the fabric, i.e. its appearance and the way in which it will perform in use. It is therefore proposed to discuss the various fibre properties and relate these to the way in which they will influence the performance of the fabric containing them, considering also the effects of yarn structure and fabric structure.

However, for those who require them the numerical values of the different properties of each fibre are set out in the table later in this chapter.

Fibre Dimensions

In the case of man-made fibres it is possible to control the physical and chemical properties of the fibres so that one day's production is similar to another's or even the next year's. As explained, the thickness of a fibre is determined at the extrusion stage and the length of staple depends on the appropriate setting of the cutting or breaking machine. However, in the case of the natural fibres, the properties vary according to climatic conditions, one crop differing from another and the fibres in the same crop also varying.

A textile fibre is characterized by flexibility, fineness and a high ratio of length to thickness. The fact that a fibre is many times longer than its width means that the fibres can be twisted together to form a yarn. The fibres can be infinitely long as in the continuous yarns or of much shorter lengths as in staple fibre. However, they should not be less than 12 mm or the fibres will not hold together to produce a yarn. The natural fibres will vary in length between certain limits: wool, for example, varies between 50 and 375 mm, whereas flax varies between 300 and 500 mm. The staple length of cotton varies between 12 and 65 mm.

The width of fibres can also vary between considerable limits. Fine fibres such as silk give delicate fabrics whereas coarse fibres like jute are used for heavy sackings. A measurement of the fineness of a yarn is given by the weight of a given length. Using the modern system, the tex is the weight in grams of a kilometre of yarn. The older unit was denier, the weight in grams of 9000 m.

Tex = grams per km; Decitex = grams per 10 km; Denier = grams per 9000 m.

Strength, Extensibility and Elasticity

These three properties are best considered collectively since there is a great deal of interaction between them.

Tensile Strength   The tensile strength is the breaking-strength of a material and is usually expressed as force per unit cross-sectional area. It is therefore a measurement of the ability of a yarn to resist breakage under the action of an applied force.

When a single fibre is considered the strength is referred to as the tenacity.

$$\text{Tenacity} = \frac{\text{breaking load}}{\text{mass per unit length}}$$

Tenacity is normally expressed in centinewtons per tex (cN per tex). Previously the units of grams per tex or grams per denier were used. Since tensile strength is related to cross-sectional area, two fibres with equal tenacities will have different tensile strengths if their cross-sectional areas are different.

Extensibility   When a force is applied to a fibre some slippage will occur between the molecules and this means that it will stretch. This stretching is referred to as extension and is expressed in terms of a percentage of the original length.

Figure 10.1 indicates the increase in length of a fibre when the applied load is increased.

The first part of the curve is fairly straight. There is an increase in length as greater loads are applied but in this area of the graph the stress is proportional to the strain. In this region the material is elastic and will return to its original length when the force is released. However, after this, for small increases in the load applied, there is a large increase in the extension, and the fibre begins to yield. Slippage occurs between the molecules and eventually the point is reached at

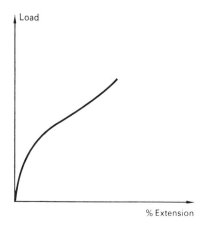

Fig. 10.1   Extensibility graph

which the fibre breaks. The toughest fibres will require the greatest load to break them.

The tensile strength and extensibility of viscose depend on the degree of orientation within the fibre. By stretching during manufacture, orientation is increased and the breaking-point can be altered. It is thus possible to produce either stronger or more elastic materials. In a highly ordered fibre the molecules will be organized and lie roughly parallel to one another. Secondary forces act between the molecules and prevent them slipping over one another. When a force is applied only a small amount of slippage can occur and thus these fibres have a fairly low extensibility. However, the load required to cause breakage will be high. On the other hand when a force is applied to a fibre with only a low degree of orientation, slippage between the molecules can occur. They slide over one another and the fibre has a high extensibility but the breaking load will be low.

In the case of nylon, however, the elastic properties are produced by stretching or cold-drawing, due to the different molecular structure.

Elasticity   When the fibre is stretched by a small amount it will return to its original length when released. Within these limits the material is said to be perfectly elastic, or to have an elastic recovery of 100 per cent. However, when greater forces are applied, permanent deformation takes place and the material can no longer recover. If a fibre returns to its original length after a 3 per cent elongation, then it is said to have an elastic recovery of 100 per cent at 3 per cent elongation. Some fibres recover more slowly than others.

In a fabric these three properties – strength, extensibility and elasticity – interact and can have varying results in the final material. For example, in wear the tearing strength of a fabric is important and this depends largely on the extensibility of the yarn and less on the tensile strength. A tightly constructed fabric woven from a strong yarn with a relatively low extensibility will usually tear more easily than a similarly constructed fabric from a yarn of lower strength but higher extensibility. At the point of tear the force is first applied to one yarn, and if this yarn cannot stretch then it must take most of the load and will eventually break. The load is then transferred to the next yarn, which will also break and so on. However, if the yarns have a high extensibility, the first yarn will stretch and some of the load will be taken by the next yarn. This in turn will also extend and again some of the load will be transferred to the adjacent yarns. Consequently, due to the fabric distortion at the point of tear, the strain will be shared by a number of yarns and greater forces will be required to tear the fabric. In a woven mixture fabric, yarns made from elastofibres will be the last to break due to their very high extensibility, despite the fact that they have a low tensile strength. For the same reason, knitted fabrics are more difficult to tear than woven fabrics.

Nylon is particularly suitable for ladies' stockings because it has suitable tensile strength, extensibility and elastic recovery. It can be stretched fairly easily at low loads so that the stockings are able to withstand the distortions of normal movements such as bending the knee. The fibre is extremely elastic. This means that it is possible to have close-fitting stockings which will return to the original shape after deformation, thus avoiding permanent distortion at the knees. The tensile strength of nylon is high and thus gives a strong fibre. Polyester fibres have an equally high tensile strength but they are more difficult to stretch and do not possess such good elastic properties, so that polyesters have not been successful in the end-use of ladies' stockings.

The Effect of Moisture

The amount of moisture absorbed by the different fibres varies considerably. Fibres absorb the moisture from the atmosphere, the amount absorbed depending upon the relative humidity of the air. The property of a fibre to absorb moisture is known as the moisture regain. This is the weight of absorbed water expressed as a percentage of the dry weight of the fibre.

$$\text{Moisture regain} = \frac{\text{weight of absorbed water} \times 100}{\text{oven-dry weight of fibre}} \text{ (per cent)}$$

The amount of moisture absorbed by certain types of viscose is almost equal to its own weight, whereas polyester fibres absorb virtually none (Table 10.1).

TABLE 10.1   WATER IMBIBITION FIGURES*
(Expressed as a percentage of fibre weight)

Standard Viscose	95
Sarille	85/95
Durafil	65/70
Vincel	65/70
Cotton	50/60
Wool	40
Acetate	25/30
Tricel	11/12
Nylon	11/12
Acrylic	8/9
Polyester	11/12

*Water Imbibition – the weight of water retained after completely wetting and centrifuging a sample at 1000 g for 5 minutes (expressed as a percentage of the bone-dry weight of the fibre used.)

Polar groups, such as hydroxyl groups, attract water molecules. The amount of water absorbed by a textile fibre will thus depend on the presence of such polar groups and also on their accessibility. Cellulose contains many polar groups but the strong cross-linking between cellulose chains in the organized crystalline areas means that the chains cannot separate and the hydroxyl groups are not accessible. However, in the amorphous areas there are relatively few points of attraction between the chains and the polar groups are accessible. Water can thus be absorbed and can sometimes break the linking between the chains and result in loss of fibre strength.

It is generally recognized that if a garment is to be comfortable when worn close to the skin, it must either absorb perspiration or allow it to pass through the fabric. Cellulosic fibres such as cotton and viscose and protein fibres such as wool contain polar groups and will absorb perspiration from the body without feeling damp in wear. These fibres are thus more comfortable in very hot climates (Chapter 12). The synthetic fibres such as nylons, polyesters and acrylics have lower moisture regains and are virtually non-absorbent. Care is needed when producing fabrics from these fibres to ensure that the construction of the material allows perspiration to pass through the fabric. The early nylon shirtings were made from a closely woven fabric, which did not allow the moisture to pass through it in order to evaporate. The nylon shirtings now available are usually knitted fabrics, which permit some transmission of moisture and may therefore, be more comfortable to wear. The fact that the synthetics continue to be used for underwear indicates that the garments are acceptable in a temperate climate.

The fact that these fibres absorb very little moisture is of great advantage during washing. During wear, water-borne stains will not penetrate the fibres to the same extent as with natural fibres and they are therefore easily removed during washing. The garments made from synthetic fibres will also dry quickly due to the small moisture uptake by the fibres. Spin-drying a light-weight nylon article will remove a large percentage of the moisture and leave it almost 'dry'. Nylon stockings, underwear and shirts can be washed out and left to drip-dry overnight. These advantages of easy washing and drying are of benefit to the consumer and probably explain the use of these fibres in many of the above applications.

Since most man-made fibres absorb little moisture they have a high electrical resistance. This means that static charges can be formed on garments, particularly underslips and skirt linings that hang freely. Fibre producers are using more and better antistatic finishes which help prevent this build-up of charge, but these have varying degrees of permanence to washing. A final rinse in one of the proprietary softening agents also helps, though of course this is only temporary and must be repeated after every wash.

The tendency of nylon clothing to cling, crackle and feel sticky has to some extent been overcome in the new modified antistatic nylons recently introduced. The chemical polymers that form the nylon 66 and nylon 6 fibres are modified by incorporating additives which increase the electrical conductivity of the fibre. Static charges can thus leak away, thereby giving improved comfort to the wearer because of a greatly reduced tendency to cling, freedom from crackles and sparks, and reduced attraction for airborne particles of soil. The antistatic nylons also disperse moisture more quickly, and thus enable perspiration to evaporate readily. The utilization of antistatic nylons is now being extended through the whole range of nylon end-uses. Lingerie and men's shirtings were fields where the advantages of increased comfort were obvious, but more recent applications include work wear, dress fabrics, household sheets, pillowcases and knitwear. Laces are produced for the lingerie together with stretch tricot and power nets for corsetry. Trade marks used for these fibres include Celon Anti-stat, Counterstat, Enka Comfort and Ultron.

Nylon fabrics, particularly underwear and shirtings in white or pale shades, can become dingy and grey after a time due to soiling. However, since the synthetics are more hard-wearing this may only become apparent after a relatively long wear life if the garments are washed frequently. The triacetates have a moisture absorption low enough to give quick-drying, easy-care fabrics, but they also retain a good white.

The moisture absorption of a fibre will affect the processing and finishing of the yarns and fabrics made from it. Fibres which absorb reasonable quantities of water are usually easier to dye than those which absorb only small amounts. The uptake of water is accompanied by swelling and the dye molecules are able to penetrate the yarns. The degree of order within a fibre also affects the dyeing properties. Water is unable to penetrate between the molecules of a crystalline region as easily as in the amorphous areas. Increased cross-linking between molecules lowers the moisture absorption and the dye molecules are not able to migrate from the dye bath into the fibre spaces between the molecules. For this same reason highly orientated fibres are more resistant to chemical attack, since the molecules cannot penetrate the fibre, but this will be discussed in more detail subsequently.

The swelling of fibres by the uptake of water can be a disadvantage since it can sometimes cause shrinkage. Due to the swelling, the yarns are pulled closer together as shown in Fig. 10.2.

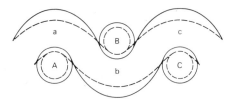

Fig. 10.2   Diagrammatic representation of the cross-section of a woven fabric

The dotted lines represent the dry yarns and the continuous lines represent the wet yarns after swelling. If the yarns A, B and C remained in the same positions then the length of yarn a, b, c, would have to increase. However, it is unlikely that the yarn will increase in length and instead yarns A and C will be pulled nearer to B. When the fabric is dry and the yarns are back to their original sizes it is possible to iron out this distortion in the case of flat fabric such as skirts and curtains. It is not so easy to obtain a good result on such areas as the neckband of a shirt. Finishes are now applied to both cotton and viscose fabrics in order to reduce the moisture absorption, and creasing during the washing process. The modern resin finishes have been discussed in Chapter 9 and are referred to as 'minimum-care' or 'easy-care' finishes. The synthetic fibres will not take up moisture or swell. They thus have a good crease-recovery and give easy-care fabrics that dry quickly, without the application of a finish.

See Fig. 10.3 for illustration of fabric distortion due to fibre swelling.

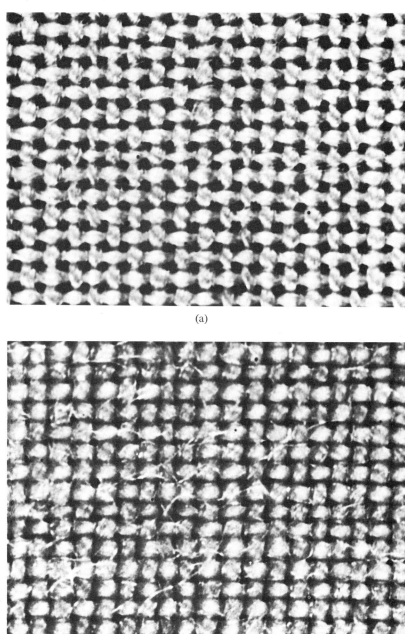

(a)

(b)

Fig. 10.3   Fabric distortion as a result of fibre swelling: (a) viscose dry; (b) viscose wet

The Effect of Heat

All fibres are affected by heat in some way, but for different fibres the tempera-tures that cause damage vary and so do the effects. When subjected to relatively high temperatures, cotton scorches and wool decomposes, whereas the synthetic fibres soften at lower temperatures and melt before decomposing. The sensitivity to heat of a fibre is a most important consideration in the laundering and ironing processes, where it is necessary to restore the article to its clean and original state without undue deterioration. It is necessary to use different temperatures for washing and different settings on irons, and these should be given on care labels attached to the article. The different methods of giving this advice to the con-sumer are discussed in some detail in Chapter 13 on labelling.

The cellulosic fibres have a relatively good resistance to degradation by heat. Cotton and linen fabrics can thus be washed at the highest temperature setting of 95°C or more, and can, in fact, be boiled, although this technique is rarely used today. To get a good white cotton article it is necessary to use a temperature of 95°C or more, to obtain the maximum action from the perborate bleach present in most heavy-duty washing powders. Cotton and linen fabrics require the highest iron setting, for the heat to be sufficient to remove the creases and give a good finish. Viscose will also withstand fairly high temperatures, being a cellulosic fibre and, depending on the article, recommended washing temperatures are usually about 60°C and the warm iron setting is required. However, a lower washing temperature is required if the viscose has special finishes applied to it or if the colours are only fast at 40°C.

The protein fibres are more sensitive to heat and wool becomes weak and loses its soft handle when heated in boiling water for some length of time. The combination of very hot water and mechanical action causes the wool to felt. This is due to the presence of scales on the wool fibre and is fully dealt with under the section on shrinkage. It is recommended to wash wool at 40°C with the minimum amount of agitation in a machine and avoid rubbing by hand. Wool scorches as a result of the heat from a very hot iron and it is, therefore, recommended that wool is ironed on the warm setting. Silk will withstand higher temperatures than wool when heated dry, but for washing a water temperature of about 40°C is recom-mended and the warm iron setting. The fabric should always be ironed on the reverse side.

Other fibres, including acetate, triacetate and the synthetics such as nylons, polyesters and acrylics, are all thermoplastic. Thermoplasticity is the property of a fibre to soften and melt when sufficiently high temperatures are reached. In this state the fibre is plastic, the molecules can move and the shape can be altered by external forces. When the fibre cools it becomes hard again and the new shape is permanent until sufficiently high temperatures are reached and cause the material to become plastic again. This property can be used to great advantage in bulking, permanent pleating and heat-setting, but care must obviously be taken during wear, washing and using to ensure that such temperatures are not reached. In Table 10.2 showing properties, information is given about which fibres are thermoplastic, but the softening temperatures will vary according to the chemical composition and the organization of the various fibres.

The washing temperature of these fabrics must not be too hot but the most important fact is that they must not be creased while in a softened state. If a fabric

TABLE 10.2 FIBRE PROPERTIES

Class of fibre	Density	Tenacity cN/tex		% Extensibility		Water imbibition expressed as a % of fibre weight	Thermoplastic
		Dry	Wet	Dry	Wet		
Cotton*	1.54	–	–	–	–	50–60	No
Wool*	1.32	–	–	–	–	40	No
Acetate	1.32	10–12	5–7	20–30	35–45	25–30	Yes
Acrylic	1.15–1.21	16–32	15–24	35–45	40–50	8–9	Yes
(High tenacity)		40–44	35–40	25–30	27–32		
Alginates	1.78	14–18	4	2–6	25	150	No
Chlorofibres	1.35–1.72	8–27	8–27	12–150	12–150	0	Yes
Elastanes	1.0–1.26	6–7	6–7	550–600	550–600	3	Yes
Glass	2.5–2.7	56–62	48–51	3–4	2.5–3.5	–	Yes (but at much higher temperatures than other thermoplastic fibres)
Metallic	–	4–8	–	30–40	30–40	5	No
Modacrylic	1.30–1.36	26–31	25–29	26	27	15–20	Yes
Nylon	1.14	40–51 (High tenacity yarns 62–80)	35–47	30–40	40–50	11–12	Yes
Polyester	1.38	31–49	31–49	20–40	20–40	11–12	Yes
Polyethylene	0.92–0.95	13–53	13–53	25–50	25–50	0	Yes
Polypropylene	0.91	35–53 (High tenacity 70–75)	35–53	20	20	0	Yes
Standard viscose	1.51	17–26	8–13	18–30	20–40	95–105	No
Modified viscose							
High tenacity filament	1.51	35–66	25–49	4.5–17	6.5–33	65–75	No
Modal, high wet modulus fibres	1.51	30–40	21–27	8–14	11–19	65–70	No
Crimped	1.51	15–21	7–13	18–40	25–55	85–95	No
Triacetate	1.30	10–13	6–7	25–35	30–40	10–12	Yes

* Figures have not been given for the strength and extensibility of these two natural fibres, because their properties vary according to the conditions of growth, variety of plant or sheep, grazing land, etc., and thus cover a wide range of values as explained in Chapter 2.

made from a thermoplastic fibre is taken out of hot water and then cooled in a crumpled state, as in a spin-drier, permanent creases will be set in. It is, therefore, necessary to give these fabrics a final cold rinse before a short spin. Thermoplastic fibres must also be ironed at a lower setting or the heat will be sufficient to melt them. The recommended washing and ironing temperatures for the different classes of fibres are give in the chapter on care labelling, but these should only be taken as a guide and may vary from garment to garment due to the method of making-up. The advice given on a care label should always be followed.

The property of thermoplasticity enables fabrics to be heat-set. Strains are imposed on fabrics during processing and these result in shrinkage, when the fabric is washed and the tensions can relax. However, with thermoplastic fibres these strains can be nullified by heat treatment and the fabric then becomes quite stable and will not shrink unless the temperature reached approaches that used to set the fabric.

The property of thermoplasticity also means that the fibres can be modified by bulking. The straight filaments of continuous filament yarns are twisted in some way so that they are looped. As a result of a heat treatment, the filaments can then be set in their various helices, and the resultant yarn is a mass of tangled filaments. The bulk of the yarn is increased and air is entrapped. Fabrics thus have a warmer handle and are more similar to those made from spun yarns. These techniques are discussed in more detail in the section on bulked yarns in Chapter 4. These fabrics are more comfortable to wear because perspiration can pass through the fabric to the outside of the garment.

The idea of creasing and setting fabrics has been developed and is now the basis of the permanent pleating of fabrics such as the triacetates. The fabric is subjected to a heat treatment when folded or creased in the desired form. It is then cooled down in the same position and the pleats or creases imposed will be permanent unless temperatures are approached similar to those at which the pleats were set in. In the case of permanently pleated garments it is recommended to give a hand-hot final rinse and then hang to dry so that the pleats can fall into place.

The way in which a fibre burns in a flame may be used as a guide to the identification of fibres. The cellulosic fibres such as cotton and viscose char and burn, leaving a grey flaky ash. Wool burns in the flame, but does not continue to do so when removed from the flame, each fibre forming a charred black ball. In general, the thermoplastic fibres will melt and drop away from the flame but this test is discussed further in Chapter 15, on identification.

Shrinkage

One of the problems encountered in laundering is that of shrinkage, resulting in a reduction in size of the article, possibly accompanied by a thickening of the fabric and an alteration in handle. There are essentially two different forms of shrinkage – felting shrinkage and relaxation shrinkage – but fabric distortion can also take place as a result of fibre swelling. However, the latter can often be corrected by ironing.

Felting Shrinkage   Felting shrinkage only occurs with wool and other animal fibres when the fabric is subjected to mechanical action while it is wet. The fibres become matted together in a consolidated mass and the appearance and handle of the fabric are completely altered as the fabric shrinks. Much work has been carried out on the felting of wool and it now seems certain that the scales on the surface of the animal fibres play an important part, although the mechanism is not completely understood.

The scales on a wool fibre all point towards the tip of the fibre and fibres will be roughly in the tip-to-root direction. Wool fibres will, therefore, be able to move more easily through a tangled mass of fibres in one direction only, travelling root first. It has been suggested that felting shrinkage is due to the movement of fibres and because of the scales, knots and entanglements will eventually be formed.

Felting seems to be increased by mechanical action, as received in washing-machines and particularly by any form of rubbing. Some woollen fabrics felt more readily than tightly woven worsted fabrics.

Chemical processes are now available to produce wool that will not felt. Most of these depend on altering the surface of the wool fibres so that the scales are no longer effective and the fibres can travel in both directions. Examination under the electron microscope shows that the edges of the scales are more rounded. One such method involves attacking the surface of the wool with chlorine, but care has to be taken to ensure that the attack is restricted to the surfaces of the scales and the wool immediately below them. The oldest method involved treatment of the wool with an acidified sodium hypochlorite solution but newer techniques use dry chlorine gas. This second method has the advantage that it is possible to obtain a more even treatment, but both chlorine treatments tend to give a harsh handle.

An anti-felting treatment for wool using potassium permanganate and sodium hypochlorite solutions is being used in Britain and leaves the articles with a softer handle.

Felting can also be prevented by applying a resin finish to the wool. The resin holds the fibres in place and prevents their movement through the fibre mass.

Wool articles will sometimes felt in wear when subjected to mechanical friction in moist conditions, and particularly good examples are socks worn for sport. These articles require fairly severe anti-felting treatments if they are to be satisfactory in use.

Relaxation Shrinkage or Strain Recovery Fibres and yarns are subjected to tensions in processing and it is impossible to dye and finish a fabric without stretching it to some extent. At the end of processing, the finisher attempts to remove this stretch so that the fabric will not shrink during the first wash. It is very difficult completely to relax a fabric made from a non-thermoplastic yarn such as cotton or viscose without altering the appearance and handle. The shrinkage which occurs on washing if the relaxation has not been complete is known as 'relaxation shrinkage'. Much of this relaxation shrinkage will take place in the first laundering, but the full shrinkage may not always be produced until after two or three washes.

Unlike felting shrinkage, relaxation shrinkage can occur with all fibres, since it is merely a relaxation of the strains imposed during manufacture. With thermo-plastic fibres it is possible to heat-set the fabric so that it is quite stable in the slightly stretched state and will not shrink on washing.

Fabric Distortion as a Result of Fibre Swelling It has been stated previously that the absorption of moisture can cause swelling of the yarns.

In a tightly woven construction the yarns will be pulled in together as a result of this swelling and the fabric will become distorted. This can be corrected by ironing flat fabrics, but can cause problems in such areas as neckbands.

Chemical Resistance

The processing of yarns and fibres involves the use of numerous chemicals including detergents, bleaching agents, scouring agents and others used during dyeing and finishing. The aim in using all these substances is to bring about the necessary reactions without seriously harming the fibres themselves. The way in which a fibre will react to a given chemical depends on the chemical composition of the polymer and on the fibre structure. The notes below indicate which fibres are particularly susceptible to attack from specific chemicals.

Effect of Acids   The cellulosic fibres, cotton, linen and viscose, are sensitive to the action of acids. Care must be taken to wash off acid quickly and not allow it to dry into the fabric. Even dilute acid, if allowed to dry on to the fabric, can cause disintegration of the fibres. The acid hydrolyses the cellulose chain and breaks it down into shorter lengths. The final stage of this breakdown would be the reduction to single glucose units.

Protein fibres are more resistant to the action of acid. Dilute solutions of mineral acids cause swelling of the wool fibre, but wool can be boiled in 2 or 5 per cent solutions of sulphuric acid with no great damage to the fibre after one hour. Higher concentrations may decompose wool and organic acids can cause intense swelling of the fibres.

Acetate is unaffected by dilute solutions of weak acids but is attacked by strong acids in concentrated solutions.

Nylon is decomposed by hot mineral acids, and the fibres disintegrate in hot solutions of hydrochloric or sulphuric acid of 5 per cent strength.

Polyesters are resistant to many acids but are decomposed by concentrated sulphuric acid.

The acrylic fibres have good resistance to acid.

Effect of Alkalis   Alkaline cleaning agents are widely used and it is therefore important to appreciate their action on certain fibres. The cellulose fibres, cotton and linen, have an excellent resistance to alkalis. Cotton and linen fabric can be washed repeatedly in detergent solutions without being damaged and although they will swell in caustic soda, as in mercerization, this will not harm the fibre.

Viscose is resistant to dilute alkali but strong solutions will cause swelling and degradation of standard viscose, although Polynosics have a greater resistance. Acetate is not attacked by dilute solutions but strong alkalis will cause saponification, the acetate groups being replaced by hydroxyl groups. Protein fibres such as wool are particularly sensitive to alkalis, and wool will dissolve in dilute caustic soda solutions.

Nylon is not attacked by alkalis and can be boiled in concentrated sodium hydroxide solution without being damaged.

Polyesters and acrylics also have a great resistance to weak alkalis, but are attacked by strong, hot solutions.

Oxidizing Agents   Oxidizing agents are commonly used in bleaches and cleansing materials, but should always be used with great care since all textile fibres are sensitive to attack by oxidation. The housewife often does not realize the severe damage that can be caused by successive use of concentrated household bleaches.

Dilute solutions of hypochlorite are used at room temperature to bleach cotton, linen and viscose, but increases in the temperature cause severe attack on the cellulose itself. Hypochlorite bleaches damage the protein fibres, as a result of chlorine retention.

Hydrogen peroxide is used in dilute alkaline solutions but care must be taken when using this on wool. The repeated bleaching of articles such as cotton sheets will have a weakening effect upon the fabric, but this must be anticipated and allowed for in the expected wear life, if dirty articles are to be restored to a good white. This weakening will be the result of a build-up after many washes, and bleaching treatments. However, a single excessive treatment or local spillage of bleach will cause severe damage, particularly if allowed to dry in. The holes may develop during the next wash although no damage is immediately apparent.

The acrylic and polyester fibres are resistant to oxidizing agents but nylon can be damaged by either hypochlorites or peroxides.

Organic Solvents The cellulosic fibres, including cotton, linen and viscose, and the protein fibres, such as wool and silk, are all unaffected by the organic solvents used as the common dry-cleaning materials. They can be spotted with solvents such as carbon tetrachloride, trichlorethylene and acetone, and dry-cleaned in the normal way without danger of fibre damage, although care should be taken to make sure that any print on the fabric will not 'rub-off'.

Acetate, however, swells or dissolves in several solvents such as acetone and chloroform and must not be spotted with these to remove stains.

Tricel is swollen by acetone and trichlorethylene (Triklone), which must never be used for cleaning or spotting purposes. Perchlorethylene, white spirit, benzene and carbon tetrachloride can be used on Tricel without risk of damage.

Nylons and polyesters are resistant to most organic solvents but nylon will dissolve in some phenols and 90 per cent formic acid and Terylene will be dissolved by some phenolic compounds. The acrylic fibres are also resistant to most common solvents but since they are heat-sensitive, when tumbler-drying after cleaning, the temperature must be controlled and kept below a certain level or damage will occur.

Attack by Insects and Micro-organisms

Cellulose and protein are natural substances which serve as food for certain organisms.

The cellulose of cotton is attacked by fungi and bacteria. Cotton that has been treated with starch is readily attacked by mildews which weaken the fabric, give it a musty smell and leave a characteristic stain.

The protein of wool is food for many insects, including moths and beetles. The larvae of these insects feed on the wool, leaving holes in the articles and causing a great deal of damage. The clothes-moth is the most destructive of these insects and the tiny holes that it chews in wool articles can cost the owner a fortune. Moth-proofing depends on the association of chemicals with the wool fibre which make it unpalatable or poisonous to the moth. Insecticides, such as Dieldrin, are often used and these actually kill the insect. A less effective method of control is to keep chemicals, such as naphthalene, which repel the moths, near to the clothes. These moth-repellents do not kill the moth but aim at persuading it to rear its young elsewhere!

The acetates and synthetic fibres cannot serve as food for the moth grubs and in general their resistance to attack by micro-organisms is high.

Crease Recovery

It is obviously desirable that fabrics used for apparel should have a good crease recovery. Crease recovery is very much a property of the fabric since materials that will crease readily are easily made from yarns and fibres which have good crease recovery properties. The structure of the fabric is most important. Tightly woven fabrics such as taffetas are far more likely to crease than loosely constructed or knitted fabrics. This is due to the fact that in the looser constructions the strains of creasing can be spread and are not taken by short lengths of yarns which would then be badly distorted. The crease recovery of fabrics can be improved by the application of finishes, as for cottons and viscose, but the newer fibres such as nylons, acrylics and polyesters have good crease recovery properties and fabrics made from them can be quite satisfactory without these finishes.

Handle

The handle of a fabric is a property that is extremely difficult to define. Words such as 'handle', 'draping quality', 'fullness' and 'paperiness' are all used to describe fabrics, but they may be regarded as particular aspects of stiffness. An apparatus has been designed which may be used to determine the 'flexural rigidity' and the 'bending-length' of a fabric sample. The flexural rigidity is a measure of the resistance of the cloth to bending by external forces. It is related to the stiffness experienced when a fabric is handled. A cloth having a high flexural rigidity tends to feel stiff. The bending-length, on the other hand, determines the way in which a fabric drapes. This is related to the stiffness that is appreciated by visual examination of the draped fabric. A cloth having a high bending-length tends to drape stiffly.

Warmth

The warmth of a fabric is due to the insulation provided by the air trapped between the fibres and yarns, air being a relatively good insulator. The thermal insulation of the textile fibres themselves is insignificant compared with the much greater effect of the air. Thus a 'hairy' fibre can be made into warm fabrics in which much air is entrapped. This subject is dealt with in more detail in Chapter 12, when the topic is discussed in relation to the comfort of clothing.

Flammability

The flammability of textiles is a most controversial subject that often evokes deep emotional feeling when discussed. Regulations, particularly for garments, have been proposed and in some measure applied. It is forbidden by law to sell ready-made night-dresses for children under thirteen (except new-born babies) unless they are flame-resistant, but people can, of course, buy highly flammable materials by the yard for home dressmaking. Textiles will not catch fire unless they are exposed to a source of ignition, which means that in normal atmospheres spontaneous combustion is impossible. Hence, complete protection from naked flames and heaters would prevent deaths resulting from burning clothes of children and old ladies. However, this is an ideal and people continue to be exposed to the dangers of fire. Several materials are available with varying degrees of resistance to flame, ranging from 'low flam' fabrics to others which are inherently and permanently flame-resistant.

The British Standards Institution have defined the terms, and set out methods of test for flame-resistant materials in B.S. 5438. This is a revised Flammability Test method and replaces B.S. 3119 and B.S. 2963.

A flame-resistant fabric is defined as one which either will not burn, or will burn so slowly as to allow time to extinguish the flame or discard the burning fabric, and thus obviate severe injury to the wearer.

The flame-resistance rating of a fabric is derived from flammability testing and is equal to the time in seconds necessary for the propogation of flame over a distance of one hundred inches in a vertical strip of fabric. A fabric referred to as of low flammability is required to have a flame-resistance rating of one hundred and fifty or more, or be reported as being 'self-extinguishing' or 'flame not propagated'.

Different British Standard publications define the performance requirements for fabrics produced for particular end-uses. B.S. 5722 sets out the performance requirements for sleepwear. B.S. 5651 defines the wetting and cleansing procedure for assessing the durability of flame-resistant fabrics in sleep wear. Pure finished nylon, polyester and modacrylics are exempted from this durability assessment. Performance requirements are also to be devised for the end-uses of curtains and upholstery. All performance standards will be based on the test method given in B.S. 5438. A code of practice concerning the manufacture of tents will be available.

There are two groups of fabric to be considered. Those with inherent properties which give them a high flame-resistance rating and those which, although not inherently flame-resistant, have been given this property by chemical treatment. It is essential that finishes applied during manufacture should have a life comparable with that of the garment. The durability of a chemical finish on a material will, however, depend on the way in which it is treated, particularly during washing. There is at present no known chemical treatment that is entirely unaffected by all washing processes, and if the flammability properties of the fabric are deleteriously affected by bleaching, the precautionary advice 'do not bleach' must be given.

Nylon is described as flame-resistant and is widely used for children's nightdresses, as it complies with the Home Office safety regulations. The recommended standards cover not only the flame-resistance rating of the fabrics, but also the style of garment and the trimmings used. It is essential to avoid the use of flammable ribbons, sewing threads, etc.

Teklan is the registered trade mark for the modacrylic fibre manufactured by Courtaulds Ltd, and is inherently flame-retardant. Fabrics with permanently flame-retardant properties can therefore be produced in 100 per cent Teklan. Other modacrylic fibres include Acrilan SEF and Kanekaron.

It is possible to modify cellulose acetate fibres in order to reduce their flammability. These fibres can be used to produce fabrics of low flammability but they are not at present being manufactured commercially.

The degree of flammability of the fabric produced will depend, amongst other things, on the fabric weight and construction, the fibre denier and the treatment to which the material has been subjected. Tests must, therefore, always be made on samples of the finished fabric to confirm the actual flammability rating.

Cotton and viscose are available in treated forms, which then pass the regulations for low flammability. The leading finishers in this field are Proban, and the actual process involves impregnating the cotton and viscose with specific organic phosphorus compounds. Proban maintains a rigorous testing routine to ensure that cloth finished by its licensees reaches the required standards and is sufficiently fast to washing. The finish will withstand normal dry-cleaning and laundering, but not bleaching. The accumulation of lime-soap deposits on the fabric as a result of poor rinsing impairs the efficiency of the finish, and appropriate warnings, recommending not to wash in soap in hard-water areas, should be given. The early treated winceyettes had a rather harsh feel but this problem has now been overcome. The cost of the fabric is, of course, increased by the finishing process.

Another finish which imparts flame-resistant properties is Pyrovatex, produced by Ciba-Geigy.

11. Uses – Suitability for Purpose

THE properties of a fabric will influence its performance in actual use and determine its suitability for a given purpose. There is no ideal fibre, possessing every advantageous property, and suitable for every end-use. This is the very reason why there are so many different fibres, and modifications of these, on the market today. The various fibres and fabrics available each have their own particular properties and it is necessary to select the most suitable ones for a given end-use.

It is proposed to consider the use of textiles according to the end-use as follows:

(i) Clothing, including fashion articles.
(ii) Carpets, furnishings and upholstery.
(iii) Household linen.
(iv) Industrial.

It must be remembered however that the way in which the fibre is made up into a fabric can greatly influence the fabric properties, as explained in Chapter 10. The mixing and blending of different fibres can produce fabrics in which the advantages of each fibre are incorporated.

CLOTHING, INCLUDING FASHION ARTICLES

In this section of the industry the aesthetic appeal is all-important, particularly in high-fashion garments. The customer is greatly influenced by the appearance of the article, its design, colour and handle, but the discerning woman may demand fashion in practical, easy-care garments at realistic prices.

The consideration of important properties will depend on the circumstances of use. In a hot climate the ability of the fibre to absorb moisture might be thought of as a most important consideration, and a light-weight cotton fabric selected for a night-dress or for underwear. However, in this country many people use nylon fabrics, which will not absorb moisture but do allow the perspiration to pass through them, and accept this level of comfort because of the additional advantages of the easy washability and quick-drying properties.

The range of fibres available for use in clothing is so enormous that in this text it is only possible to cover briefly the main uses of the most important fibres.

Cotton

Cotton garments give good durability and can withstand hard wear and re-peated washing. They are able to absorb perspiration and for this reason some people find them more comfortable in wear. It is possible to produce a whole range of cotton fabrics, which are strong, hard-wearing and versatile. Cotton is therefore made into every type of garment, including dresses, shirts and under-wear. The finer yarns can be made into tightly woven fabrics such as poplins and voiles, which have the crisp attractive handle associated with cotton. The coarser yarns are used in drills and denims, which are heavier, hard-wearing fabrics often used in jeans.

Cotton is also widely used in blends with most other fibres, including wool, viscose, polyester and acrylic fibres.

The fact that untreated cotton absorbs moisture readily means that it will take longer to dry and require more ironing than the newer man-made fibres. How-ever, resin treatment can be used to produce cotton fabrics with drip-dry, non-iron finishes.

Wool

The fact that wool fibres are crimped and resilient means that they hold together well when spun and air is trapped between them. Air is a good insulating material and woollen fabrics can be very warm particularly when the fabric has a lofty, open structure with large quantities of air entrapped within it. The elasticity and resilience of the fibres stops them bedding down easily and minimizes crushing and creasing. By increasing the amount of twist in the yarn it is possible to make strong yarns such as worsteds for men's suitings and for ladies' dresses and suit fabrics. On the other hand it is possible to make yarns without twisting them very tightly and the fibres will still hold together and give a reasonably strong yarn. Knitting wools are loosely spun and when knitted up into jumpers and cardigans are warm due to the insulating value of the entrapped air.

Wool fibres are in fact poor conductors of heat but this is not the important factor in determining the total insulating value of the fabric. This is determined by the air trapped between the fibres. Thus other fibres, if given the same type of crimp so that equal quantities of air were trapped in the fabric, would be equally warm in wear.

Wool is widely used in all types of clothing, including outerwear and under-wear. It will readily absorb moisture from the atmosphere or perspiration from the skin and in doing this a woollen garment will generate heat. This is the reason why flannel underwear was so popular. The value of having warm but 'damp' flannel next to the skin is, however, a debatable point and will be discussed in Chapter 12, on the 'Comfort of Clothing'.

Wool is used in knitted articles such as cardigans and jumpers. These can be soft and warm, and, since the fibre absorbs moisture, there is no problem of static accumulating as with the newer synthetic fibres. However, untreated woollen jumpers cannot be washed and dried with the same ease as the synthetic fibres. After several washings woollen garments are liable to shrink or felt to some extent. Treatments are now available which, when applied to wool, prevent it from shrinking if the recommended washing instructions are followed. Some wool garments are now described as 'machine washable', although the amount of agitation used in washing must often be kept to a minimum.

Silk

Silk is expensive and difficult to produce and can thus be regarded as a luxury fibre. Women like the aesthetic qualities of silk, its soft, beautiful handle and attractive appearance, and are therefore willing to pay the price. Silk can be woven or knitted into a wide range of beautiful fabrics including sheer chiffons, woven prints with the characteristic scroop as the material rubs together, and rich, heavy pile velvets. The material is used in fashion articles such as ladies' dresses, but silk is a delicate fibre and is easily damaged.

The fabric does not have the advantages of easy washability with little or no ironing, and it is not resistant to degradation by perspiration. These points have to be sacrificed for the aesthetic appeal of beautiful fabrics.

Viscose

Viscose is produced in large quantities, a substantial percentage of production being in staple form. It is inexpensive and versatile, and is thus used in almost every end-use, soft or firm fibres for fashion, stronger ones for tyres, more springy ones for carpets, and so on. Viscose is perhaps the nearest of all to the 'universal fibre', and is used in all types of clothing. The many new viscose fibres of today are certainly very different from the original 'artificial silk'.

The versatility of viscose is illustrated by the different types of fabrics produced from it. In continuous filament form viscose can be used to produce smooth, shiny lining fabrics or light-weight organdie fabrics, but higher-denier staple can be used to produce heavy tweeds. Viscose can also be used for making velvets.

In addition to standard viscose there is now available the whole new range of Courtauld's modified viscose fibres.

Vincel This is a modified viscose with many of the characteristics of fine-quality cotton. It can be used alone or in blend with cotton, Terylene, Dacron, Courtelle or nylon to make a variety of fabrics for dresses, rain wear, shirts, woven and knitted lingerie and underwear.

Sarille Sarille fibres have been given a permanent crimp and can therefore be used to produce fabrics with a full, warm handle and built-in crease recovery. Sarille can be used alone or in blend with wool to give a range of fabrics suitable for dresses, suits, rain wear and fleece fabrics.

Viloft This high-bulk hollow fibre can be used in combination with polyester in spun yarns. The cellulosic fibre imparts comfort and absorbency to the fabric and the polyester component gives added strength. Fabrics made from Viloft have a firmer handle than similar materials made from standard viscose fibres. Apparel end-uses include shirts, blouses and jersey fabrics for dress wear.

The new fibres possess characteristics and properties that are different from those of the well-known conventional viscose. For example, the wet strength can be improved. The well-known phrase 'weaker when wet' is a generalization that can no longer be applied to the whole range of viscose fabrics available, although the statement may be relevant for some light-weight fabrics.

Like cotton, viscose is cellulosic and will therefore absorb moisture. In order to produce viscose fabrics with easy-care properties it is necessary to apply drip-dry, permanent-press, non-iron or crease-resistant finishes.

Viscose is not heat sensitive and can therefore be ironed with a hot iron. The general resistance to chemicals is good, which means that viscose and viscose blends can be used when a non-static, fairly resistant fabric is required.

Acetate and Triacetate

Acetate – Dicel, Lansil   Acetate fabrics can have a rich handle and an appearance resembling silk, and are therefore used extensively in fashion garments, where the aesthetic appeal is important. Typical fabrics include luxurious satins and brocades for evening dresses and formal wear. Woven fabrics such as printed taffetas and surahs, plain-dyed organzas and slub fabrics are used for day dresses, as are warp-knitted fabrics. The latter have the advantage of packing into a small space without crushing. The trade mark of the British Celanese acetate is Dicel.

Triacetate – Tricel, Arnel, Rhonel   Triacetate fibres are also used for fashion clothes, including dresses and blouses, where the easy-care properties are a great advantage. Tricel fabrics wash easily, dry quickly and need little or no ironing. They are also crease-resistant and, particularly the knitted jersey dress fabrics, can be packed into a small space without being crushed, a great advantage when travelling. Triacetates are thermoplastic and can therefore be heat-set, to give permanent pleats in garments.

Tricel can be used to produce medium-weight double-jersey fabrics, which have a lustrous appearance and a soft handle, with good stretch recovery. The double-jersey fabrics are suitable for dresses and suits. High-bulk Tricel yarns are used in all kinds of knitwear including jumpers, cardigans and casual shirts.

Nylon – Blue C Nylon, Bri-Nylon, Celon, Enkalon

The end-uses of nylon include shirts, lingerie, stockings and underwear. Since nylon does not absorb much moisture garments made from it dry quickly. These garments are easily washed and can be rinsed out in the evening and hung up to dry. In the morning they are ready for wear without having to be ironed. The introduction of antistatic nylons has improved the performance and comfort of such garments, particularly lingerie, where clinging and riding-up are reduced. Nylon itself has intrinsic flame-resistant properties, so that children's night wear produced from it can be flame-resistant and comply with Home Office safety regulations. The fabric can be given a brushed surface for increased warmth.

In addition to the more traditional end-uses, nylon fabrics are also suitable for the fashion field. Dress fabrics include plain and printed warp knits and a variety of light-weight woven fabrics including chiffons and crêpes. Nylon knitwear is produced from heavier denier yarns, and jersey fabrics suitable for ladies' dresses and suits are made from high bulk yarn.

Outer fabrics with novelty cloqué or blister effects are made by laminating a nylon ciré taffeta to a layer of foam and patterning with a heated roller. Stretch fabrics suitable for anoraks or ski clothes can be made with a nylon-surface fabric.

Nylon staple is also used in mixtures with other fibres.

Acrylics – Acrilan, Courtelle, Dralon, Orlon

The acrylic fibres are extremely versatile and can be given many 'looks' according to the method of manufacture. These range from thick, chunky knits to fine jerseys and tweeds, in goods which include dresses, suitings, jumpers, sportswear, children's wear and pile fabrics.

The popularity of the acrylic fibres is probably a result of their easy-care properties. They will not shrink or felt, and only need a light pressing when washed correctly. Fabrics made from 'high-bulk' acrylic yarns are warm yet light in weight and are hard-wearing. They are intrinsically moth-proof and acid-resistant and can be dyed to any shade. For these reasons the acrylic fibres are extensively and successfully used in all types of clothing. Fabrics for suits and dresses include double and single jerseys which are ideal for everyday living and for travelling. Woven tweeds, often blends with wool, are suitable for skirts, dresses and suits. Acrylic fibres can also be used in light-weight woven fabrics in 100 per cent form and in blends with cotton and viscose. These are used for women's blouses and dresses.

Foam-backed single jersey is used in men's and women's coats and casual wear. Acrylic and wool worsted fabrics are used for men's suitings, and other applications in menswear include knitted casual shirts, acrylic/cotton underwear and casual woven shirts.

Handknitting yarns are made, both in 100 per cent form and in blends with wool. Pile fabrics are used in the warm-lining trade, and in children's matinee jackets and sleeping-bags.

Polyesters – Dacron, Lirelle, Terlenka, Terylene

Polyester fibres are now used in almost every kind of garment for man, woman or child.

Continuous filament fabrics can be sheer and light-weight because of the strength of the yarn. Taffetas, satins, brocades, voiles, organdies and other delicate dress fabrics are easily laundered.

The fibres do not absorb much moisture and thus the garment will dry quickly. Permanent creases can be heat-set into a garment since polyesters are thermo-plastic.

Double-jersey fabrics with a full handle suitable for women's suits, coats and dresses can be made by using bulked filament yarns. Bulked yarn is made from

100 per cent Terylene polyester under licence from I.C.I. Ltd, using a modified false-twist process as described on p. 73.

Polyester staple is used in blends with other fibres such as cotton, viscose and wool. Polyester/wool suitings are hard-wearing and have a good shape retention. Creases can be set in to improve the appearance. Polyester shirts are available in both 100 per cent form and in blends with cotton. The knitted filament shirts for casual wear do not need ironing, and the more formal polyester/cotton shirts need only a minimum of ironing.

Polyester and polyester/wool blend ties are on the market in addition to raincoats, topcoats and sports jackets all in polyester blends.

Elastanes – Lycra, Spanzelle

The elastane fibres are used where stretch recovery and support properties are required, incorporated in articles such as support stockings, foundation garments and swim wear. They are also used in minor percentages to give, or improve, the stretch and recovery characteristics of conventional fabrics or garments. In knitted garments, particularly those made from acrylic yarns, Lycra, Spanzelle or similar stretch yarns can be used in the neck ribs and cuffs to improve the appearance and performance.

They are also used in men's socks to give stretch to traditional wool and cotton socks. In woven fabrics the amount of elastane fibre required to give stretch recovery is very small, and the cloth characteristics, such as handle and appearance, are not affected. These yarns are used as rubber replacements, where the resistance to chemicals and perspiration which degrade rubber itself are an advantage. New fields of application are continually being developed, due to the fine denier and useful textile characteristics of the yarn.

CARPETS, UPHOLSTERY AND SOFT FURNISHINGS

During the past few years purchasing power has increased, and a large portion of this extra money is spent on house ownership, particularly on carpets, curtains and upholstery. People are also demanding more sophisticated environments requiring attractive textures, prints and colours, to which there has been a revolutionary change of attitude. The average sitting-room of fifty years ago had predominantly browns, dark greens and other practical shades, which did not show the dirt. Now fashion has come into the picture bringing with it brilliant blues, greens and oranges – in fact every colour of the rainbow. The darker shades become dirty just as quickly, it is merely that this does not show. However, with the newer man-made fibres lighter shades can be cleaned easily and are therefore no longer considered to be completely impracticable.

Carpets, upholstery and furnishings are purchased less frequently than clothing, but when the time comes, a lot of money is spent on an individual item and it is expected to last a long time. Surveying the vast ranges available the consumer is faced with a difficult and important decision, but how can we know whether the pile on the carpet is going to wear well, or whether the dye used in the curtaining has an adequate fastness to light? Buying from a reputable dealer, looking for trade names and informative labelling all help and are discussed in Chapter 13, but the choice is still a difficult one.

Carpets

When the colour has been matched and the design selected the two important considerations are price and performance in wear. For how long will a reasonable and acceptable appearance be retained? The fibre used in the pile is important, but the durability of a carpet depends largely on the pile density, that is the weight of pile per unit carpet area. Light-weight carpets are not suitable for busy living-rooms or staircases, where they will undergo a great deal of wear, but might be quite satisfactory in a spare bedroom that is not often used. The pile density depends on the closeness of the tufts and the thickness of the yarn. Carpets containing Evlan or acrylic fibre are usually heavier and denser than any alternatives at the same price level. Wool is an expensive fibre and it will therefore cost more to give a high pile-weight in 100 per cent wool. The bulk of fibre obtainable for a given price is most important.

The fibres selected for use in carpet piles must possess certain properties. Ideally a fibre should be hard-wearing and 'springy' so that the pile will not be permanently marked by a heavy object standing on it. The carpet must not soil too quickly but it is an advantage if it can be shampooed when stained.

Table 11.1 summarizes the properties required for carpets and indicates which fibres possess them, in order of merit.

TABLE 11.1   THE PROPERTIES OF A CARPET FIBRE

Property	1st	2nd	3rd	4th
Soil resistance	Wool	Evlan	Acrylic	Nylon
Ease of cleaning	Acrylic	Nylon	Evlan	Wool
Resilience	Acrylic	Wool	Nylon	Evlan
Strength	Nylon	Acrylic	Wool	Evlan
Economy	Evlan	Wool	Acrylic	Nylon

It can be seen that the fibres have different properties and the advantages are shared between them. No fibre stands out as the ideal fibre. For a hard-wearing carpet, which will retain a good appearance, will not soil too quickly and will readily clean and restore to its original state, the answer appears to be to use blends.

Typical blends include:

(1) 50 per cent wool/50 per cent Evlan
(2) 80 per cent Evlan/20 per cent nylon
(3) $42\frac{1}{2}$ per cent wool/$42\frac{1}{2}$ per cent Evlan/15 per cent nylon

(4) 50 per cent acrylic/50 per cent Evlan
(5) 80 per cent wool/20 per cent nylon
(6) 40 per cent acrylic/40 per cent Evlan/20 per cent nylon

Wool is the fibre traditionally used in carpets and is a first-class fibre for this end-use, but by itself has limitations. A high-grade carpet in 100 per cent wool will be expensive due to the cost of the wool fibre, but by blending in man-made fibres the overall cost for the same given pile density can be brought down. More than three-quarters of the carpets produced in this country are blends. The fibres are blended together to give the maximum performance and service for a given price.

Evlan is the modified viscose fibre developed specifically for the carpet trade. Evlan is sometimes used by itself, but it is usually mixed with other fibres to give a good pile density and value for money since the cellulosics, including the newer Evlan M, are low-priced fibres.

For example, in the triple blend of wool/Evlan/nylon, the traditional qualities of wool, the bulk and density of Evlan and the strength of nylon are combined to give a carpet with excellent properties and it is lower in price than the all-wool counterpart.

The acrylic fibres Acrilan, Courtelle and Orlon are soft and bulky, but hard-wearing. The resilience is heat-set into the fibre and carpets are easy to clean. Stains can be removed by sponging.

Nylon is strong and hard-wearing and is also easy to clean. It is of great value for blending with other fibres to improve the durability of the carpet. Alone it tends to generate some static and thus attract any loose fibre or fluff. Modacrylic and polypropylene fibres are also being used in carpets.

All these fibres are used both in the more traditional Axminster and Wilton carpets and in the large number of tufted carpets now made.

Development work has been carried out on certain forms of tufted carpets and felts with the aim of producing semi-hard floorings. These are intended to fill the gap between conventional hard flooring and carpets. The flooring has durability and practicability but also has warmth, texture and resilience. This is ideal for the many locations where a cold, hard surface is not acceptable – in old people's homes, air terminals, bus stations, schools and cinemas, but where hard wear must be withstood.

Upholstery and Soft Furnishings

Upholstery fabrics may also be subjected to heavy wear although this is of a different kind. The important properties of upholstery fabrics include the following:

(a) Fabric strength and seaming behaviour.
(b) Abrasion resistance.
(c) Colour fastness to light, rubbing and surface shampooing.

The abrasion resistance is most important and depends to a large extent on the fabric structure. When used properly nylon, the acrylics or Evlan provide good abrasion resistance. If moisture absorbency is low the fabric will dry rapidly after shampooing and will have resistance to water-borne stains. With absorbent fibres, finishing treatments can reduce the absorbency and give stain resistance.

Standards have been proposed for upholstery cloths and methods of testing have been devised for measuring such properties as resistance to shampooing and abrasion. The results of these tests can, to some extent, give an indication of the performance that a particular fabric will have in use.

In fabrics to be used for curtains the colour fastness to light is particularly important, as is the resistance to gas fume fading. Certain dyes, particularly in areas of atmospheric pollution, can accelerate fabric degradation and it is possible for the material to be completely lost in certain areas of a floral pattern, where one colour was present. This damage often becomes evident after washing. What appeared to be an undamaged curtain can go into holes where the degraded fabric has been washed away.

Many different fibres are used in upholstery cloths and furnishings and this short summary indicates the main ones in terms of quantity used.

Both filament and staple viscose are used in upholstery and curtainings. Viscose staple is used in many types of fabric either alone or in blends with cotton, wool, flax or other fibres. Viscose is used in the pile of velvets and bright yarns are used in brocades for drapes and upholstery. Spun-dyed viscose staple is blended with wool to produce hard-wearing moquettes of the type used in public transport. Viscose staple is used in Moygashel fabrics with the typical 'linen look'.

The amount of cotton used in upholstery cloths is very low but a lot is used for the less expensive lighter-weight curtain fabrics in addition to the more expensive designs on cotton. Cotton is used in blends with other fibres including viscose staple. Some fabrics are available in which cotton is blended with Vincel, and the usage of printed fabrics of this type is likely to increase.

A substantial amount of all the surface fibre being used in this country for upholstery fabrics, both domestic and contract, is Evlan. This modified viscose fibre was initially very successful in the carpet industry, but the excellent wearing properties of Evlan mean that it is also being used in ranges of upholstery fabrics for which it is particularly suitable. These fabrics include tweeds, plain weaves and satins. Backings applied to some 100 per cent Evlan fabrics can give an increase in abrasion resistance, but the type of backing is important as it affects the cleaning requirements. Some fabrics have a latex backing and this is softened by standard dry-cleaning fluids. Agents such as Thawpit can be used for local stain removal on a chair, but if saturated too much with fluid, the backing will be softened. Fabrics with either latex or acrylic resin backings can be shampooed and the acrylic backing will withstand dry cleaning. Evlan is being used in furnishing fabrics, usually in blends with cotton or viscose.

Acetate is used in curtainings as a filament warp with a variety of wefts including cotton, viscose and acrylics. It gives an attractive appearance and has good draping properties, but care must be taken in pressing to avoid damaging the acetate by an iron that is too hot.

The polyester fibres Terylene, Dacron and Tergal are available in a vast range of nets, which have a good light resistance and are easily rinsed out. They can be hung at the window to finish drying and as a result of these many advantages the polyesters have largely replaced cotton in net curtains. They are also used to some extent as a light-weight warp in heavier curtainings.

The use of nylon in the field of upholstery fabrics is growing rapidly particularly in knitted stretch covers. The fabrics are strong and knitted structures are used. For permanent upholstery cloths the nylon fabric is often bonded. Brushed nylon is used to some extent in self-lined furnishing fabrics.

The acrylic fibres with the advantages of shampooability, rapid drying and stability are being used increasingly in furnishing and upholstery fabrics both in 100 per cent fabrics and in blends with other fibres. Upholstery fabrics include velvet, Jacquard brocades, satins and tweed types.

Glass fabrics are used widely in the United States and there is now considerable expansion of the market in this country, particularly with the introduction of the new Beta Glass. A wide range of designs in both plain colours and patterns with surface interest is now available in addition to the floral prints.

HOUSEHOLD LINEN, TOWELS AND BLANKETS

Household Linen

Cotton is strong both in the wet condition and when dry. For this reason it wears well, withstanding repeated washings, and is a suitable fibre for sheets and pillowcases. Heavily soiled articles can be agitated in hot detergent solutions and can be bleached to keep them white. Cotton is also absorbent. It does, however, require ironing with a hot iron to give a good finish, but easy-care, all-cotton sheets are now being introduced. The cotton is given a resin treatment to give crease-resist, non-iron properties but the difficulty is to prevent this treatment tendering the fabric.

The amount of ironing required can also be reduced by including synthetic fibres in the blend. Polyester/cotton easy-care sheets, which are resinated, are being manufactured and are aimed at the top end of the market. The modified viscose fibre, Vincel, can also be used in blends for sheetings.

Linen sheets are available, as the properties of strength and absorbency make the fibre suitable for this end-use. Linen sheets are also aimed at the higher end of the trade and are generally more expensive than similar cotton sheets.

Warp-knitted nylon sheets now have a certain share of the market. They have the great advantage of easy-care properties. Sheets can be washed out easily, dried quickly and put back on to the bed without ironing. In addition to the normal smooth nylon sheet, striped and pattern effects can be created in the fabric, or it may be brushed on one side to give a warm handle.

Towels

The most important property of a fibre to be used in towels is that of absorbency, since the purpose of a towel is to dry both people and things. The cellulosic fibres, cotton, viscose, modified viscose and linen are therefore used.

Woven terry fabrics are universally used for face, hand and bath towels, and cotton is the traditional fibre in this market. However, viscose and the modified fibre Viloft are used in blend form for certain end-uses such as tea-towels and nappies. The modified viscose Vincel is being used in flat-woven tea-towels and in blends with cotton for towels. It is absorbent and gives a softer feel, although it takes longer to dry and gives a less crisp handle. Towels are now being made in rich, luxurious colours, in both plains and Jacquards.

Linen is ideal for glass-cloths and flat-woven towels, although cotton is frequently used instead. There is a rapid growth in decorative tea-towels, which are usually flat woven and made in linen. Terry tea-towels have a much smaller share of the market, but are growing in popularity.

Blankets

Any cloth for any end-use must necessarily be a compromise, blankets being no exception, and the user must decide what characteristics are required. For a blanket the primary consideration is 'warmth', which really means the property of preventing the heat generated by the body from escaping into the room. This depends, very largely, on the amount of air entrapped in the cloth, as air is a relatively good insulator. From this point of view, the construction of the blanket is more important than the nature of the fibre from which it is made. There are, however, many features required in a blanket other than warmth. A blanket must be of adequaate strength to stand up to normal usage over a long period without wearing into holes or splitting and the appearance retention must be adequate. The appearance can be altered or spoilt in several ways.

Pilling   This is the tendency of some fibres to roll into tight balls on the surface of the blanket. This is both unsightly and reduces the efficiency of the blanket.

Shedding   This means that in normal usage the blanket loses some of its fibres. Over a long period this obviously reduces the efficiency of the blanket and also leaves untidy pieces on the bedroom floor.

Crushability   The thickness of a blanket may be compressed in use and this is really a property of the resilience of the fibres from which the blanket is made.

Fading   The light fastness of the dyes used must be adequate to avoid colour loss on exposure to light.

The appearance must be retained after washing and it is an advantage if the blanket will dry quickly. The less absorbent fibres, such as the acrylics, will be best in this respect.

As mentioned earlier the construction of the blanket is important. The conventional blanket has in the past been woven. There are several new methods of producing a similar type of blanket, one of these being the Fiberwoven process explained in detail in Chapter 8. Blankets, which are light in weight and yet warm, can be made in a cellular construction with holes in them.

The traditional fibre for this end-use is wool, and it is still used quite extensively. Man-made fibres, however, are being used more and more in this market, the main types being viscose fibres, the acrylic fibres and nylon. Some fibres have great advantages in certain features but are not so good in others. Hence, the compromise referred to at the beginning. The purchaser should be conscious of this and decide which good points are required and how much she is willing to pay for them. The price of the blanket will depend on the fibres used and on the method of construction.

INDUSTRIAL USES

For an industrial application the serviceability of the material is usually all-important. Relevant properties include strength and durability, a resistance to chemical attack and rotting, and in some cases the textile must be able to withstand prolonged hot and wet conditions. The density can be an important consideration and, if the material is to be used as a coating, so is its smoothness. In these applications aesthetic properties such as drape and handle are secondary to functional ones.

Textile fibres are used extensively in industrial applications and this usage continues to expand as new fibres are developed and existing ones are modified to meet specific demands. It is impossible to cover every end-use within this chapter but the examples given illustrate the wide range of applications.

Fibre	*Industrial End-use*
Acetate	Acetate is produced as cigarette tow, and used for the production of filter-tips for cigarettes.
	Heat and sound insulation.
Acrylics	Due to their chemical resistance and strength the acrylic fibres are used for acid-resistant uniforms, epoxy piping and resins.
Alginate	Medical uses include dressings, etc., which will dissolve away in time. Laundry bags are made in polythene and stitched with alginate. This dissolves in the wash liquor and releases the dirty clothes.
Chlorofibres	Chlorofibres are used in the motor car industry for upholstery fabrics.
Glass	Glass is flame resistant and for this reason is used in theatre safety curtains and similar applications.
	The high strength of the fibre makes it suitable for the production of reinforced laminates, artificial limbs etc.
	Filter cloths.
	Carpet backings and for insulation.
	Fire-fighting equipment.
Modacrylics	Fire-fighting and protective clothing.
Nylon	The low density and smoothness of nylon mean that it is used for coating other materials.
	Nylon has a high strength and abrasion resistance and is therefore widely used for conveyor belts, fishing gear, ropes, work wear, etc.
	Tarpaulins, coated fabrics for industrial clothing, car seat-belts and sails.
Polyester	Polyesters are resistant to degradation by prolonged heating at temperatures which do not cause softening. They are therefore used for laundry-press cloths.
	Other end-uses include:
	Coated fabrics for dracones and inflatable buildings.
	Ropes and tyre cords.

	Sewing threads and work wear, where the resistance to abrasion, and strength are an advantage.
	Sails, tents in conjunction with cotton.
Polyethylene and Polypropylene	These fibres have a low moisture absorption and consequently will dry very quickly. Fibres such as Courlene are used in deck-chairs, awnings, etc.
	They are also resistant to chemicals and rotting and are used for ropes, twines, fishing nets and filtration materials.
Viscose	The absorbency of the material is of importance in many medical applications, viscose 'cotton wool', bandages and dressings.
	The versatility is illustrated by the following varied applications:
	Air filtration.
	Lint-free dusters, wipes and disposables.
	Laminated for water-cooled bearings.
	High-tenacity viscose is used in rubber reinforcements, especially motor car tyres, and in uniforms.
	Work wear.
Triacetates	The resistance of these fibres to hot, wet conditions makes them suitable for laundry-press cloths and similar uses.

12. Comfort in Wear*

THE properties of fibres, yarns and fabrics and the suitability of a particular fabric for a given end-use have been discussed in previous chapters. An attempt is now made to relate this information to the comfort of fabrics in wear. Little attention has been given to this subject in textile literature in the past, possibly because it is a complex phenomenon dependent on many influences. Some of these may be described as psychological aspects and thus vary from individual to individual.

In ancient civilizations, in addition to protection from the elements, the clothing or lack of it was related to religious beliefs, magical influences and the concept of modesty. In our present civilization in Britain the prime function of clothing is perhaps protection from the elements, but undoubtedly many other considerations influence our choice of dress, including the dictates of fashion, modesty and a desire to attract the attention and compliments of our neighbours.

During the past, and particularly in the Middle Ages, in Britain there has been a preoccupation with the necessity of keeping the body warm. It was the custom to cover the body with layers of woollen underclothes, particularly flannel, a loosely woven wool fabric. This maintained an overwarm skin, encouraging unnecessary sweating, and was usually the cause of the so-called 'flannel-rash', now almost extinct. Physicians used to treat fevers by overheating the patient, by heating the room, covering with feather bedding and then keeping the patient in thick woollen night wear. This caused profuse perspiration and worsened the condition of the patient. Until this century it was common for people, particularly children, to be dressed in many layers of clothing. The children of the poorer classes were in fact sometimes sewn into their underclothes for the winter. Apart from the temperature considerations, one can reflect on the unhygienic nature of this practice, encouraging the multiplication of bacteria and other organisms in the clothing. There was a definite tendency to over-dress and this fact in itself made people exceedingly susceptible to the slightest cold winds.

BODY AND SKIN TEMPERATURES

One often reads that the normal body temperature of a healthy person is in the region of 36°–37°C, and is fairly carefully controlled. However it has been demonstrated that the body 'thermostat' is sometimes less rigidly controlled than is generally believed.

The skin temperature itself varies a great deal in different regions. In an ordinarily dressed individual, under comfortable conditions, this may vary by 11°C or more between the trunk and the extremities of the limbs. Within limits, thermal comfort is a diffuse feeling from the body as a whole, with the exception

---

* Much of the recent work on this subject has been carried out at the Army Operational Research Establishment, Clothing and Equipment Physiology Division, Farnborough, and the author would like to thank Dr E. T. Renbourn for his help in the preparation of this chapter.

of the hands and feet. Thus under normal conditions and in the absence of wind or a draught, one is not particularly aware of differences in skin thermal comfort between various parts of the trunk. However, the amount of clothing may vary considerably, for example with double-breasted coats there will be additional layers of fabric down the front, and the skin temperature varies appreciably. In the case of the internal body temperature certain measurable differences are still present. After 'heavy' muscular exercise the internal temperature can rise to 39°C or 40°C or even more, and the same thing happens in a hot bath. It has been shown that under conditions of a temperate climate, ordinary clothing has little effect on the modes of heat loss from the body.

The skin rapidly becomes adapted to a constant and mild stimulus such as the cooling effect of removing clothes, or of a hot bath. Over long periods of time, weeks or months, many people can also become acclimatized to exposure to more marked heat or cold. People acclimatized to tropical heat are sensitive to cold exposure. By the same reasoning, people over-dressed in excessive underwear feel cold when this is taken off.

THE 'FEEL' OF FABRICS

Straight filament yarns can be used to make smooth fabrics, which when placed next to the skin remove heat rapidly by conduction and, therefore, produce a so-called cool feel or handle. This phenomenon can be noted in certain linen, silk, and synthetic filament materials. The feeling is apparent initially in articles such as underwear and linen sheets, where they are in contact with the skin, and is sometimes much emphasized. However, the skin rapidly becomes adapted to mild stimulations and is no longer sensitive to this cool feeling.

Hairy fabrics, on the other hand, such as wool and brushed nylon, feel warm on contact with the body due to the insulating air held between the fabric fibres and the skin.

THE 'WARMTH' OF FABRICS

The warmth of clothing materials is due to the high thermal insulation provided by the air trapped between the fibres and yarns, within the fabric interstices. The different textile fibres do have varying properties of thermal insulation but this effect is insignificant compared with the much greater effect of the entrapped air. Thus, the assertion that wool is warmer than cotton is only relevant in relation to the fact that crimped fibre such as wool can be made into warm fabrics in which much air is entrapped. Under ordinary conditions, there is little physiological difference between outer garments of more or less the same thickness whether they are made from natural fibre, synthetic fibres or blends. Most clothing fabrics contain about 70 per cent of air by volume, and a wool or nylon blanket about 90 per cent. An eiderdown, of feathers or wadding between two fabric layers, is soft and light, but will be very warm due to the large volume of entrapped air.

It should be realized that compressing these articles will change the functional thickness and hence the 'warmth'. Bedding placed on top of the body is only subjected to negligible pressure, but clothing is compressed over the seat and back by the body weight when sitting down. The amount of air entrapped is decreased, and at these places the garment is functionally not as warm.

Wind is a factor which affects the effective warmth of a material. Movement of the limbs produces breezes and these can become an appreciable wind during such activities as skiing. Strong winds blowing on a material can remove the relatively still layers of air on the outer surface and inside the fabric, and thus the thermal insulation of the fabric is impaired. Wind resistance is given by a thin but tightly woven fabric, an impermeable plastic or rubberized sheet or by two relatively open-weave materials used together.

THE UPTAKE OF WATER VAPOUR

Water vapour is continually being liberated from the lungs and the skin, and under normal conditions of rest it is by this evaporation that some of the heat is lost from the body. Textile materials, when suitably constructed, allow the transmission of this water vapour through the interstices to the outside. The natural fibres such as cotton, and particularly wool, absorb it. Standard viscose also readily absorbs both vapour and liquid moisture.

'SORPTION' HEAT OF CLOTHING

Materials made from wool will absorb water vapour from the atmosphere, particularly if the relative humidity is high. This absorption of water vapour results in the liberation of heat. The heat produced will be much greater for wool, a fibre of high vapour regain, than for polyesters, fibres of low vapour regain. This can be confirmed by experimenting with garments on hangers under controlled conditions, and the fact is often stressed in textile literature. However, its effect under practical conditions of life appears to be of no 'real' consequence. The important fact is how much of the free warmth is available to buffer heat loss from the body.

Scientifically designed, physiological trials have been carried out on men wearing garments and the advantages of wool found in the physical experiment could not be found under physiological conditions. This may partly be explained by the fact that the relative humidity near the skin will not be as high as the atmospheric humidity and thus in this area the absorption of water vapour, and hence the liberation of heat, is relatively slow.

THE UPTAKE OF WATER

Sweat is produced from the human body, the quantity increasing rapidly after heavy work or sport or in a hot or humid climate. If this sweat remains on the skin it produces a clammy feeling and is believed to be reabsorbed and in some way to block the glands. For comfort, therefore, this sweat must be removed. Absorbent materials such as wool, cotton and viscose will absorb the moisture.

Non-absorbent fibre materials take up liquid water by a process known as wicking.

A great deal of importance is often given to the physiological value of underwear made from absorptive fibre but in a temperate climate as in Britain, profuse sweating is unusual under normal conditions and synthetic fibre underwear is acceptable to a certain proportion of the population. The uptake of water by synthetic fibres is due to wicking only, and the free water in garments soaked with sweat would make them unpleasantly damp and produce chilling from the resulting rapid evaporation. Garments made from synthetic fibres would not therefore be suitable for use in tropical heat or for heavy manual labour, when profuse sweating is likely to take place.

When nylon materials are used for garments such as underwear and shirts the fabric construction is most important if they are to be comfortable in wear. For this reason knitted constructions are used as explained in Chapter 11 and acceptable garments for a temperate climate are produced, with the advantages of easy-care properties.

The phenomenon of wicking by synthetic fibres has been used to advantage in babies' nappies. Originally an absorbent material such as cotton terry towelling was used next to the skin with the addition, when required, of an outer water-impermeable layer, such as rubber or plastic. Owing to the quantity of liquid absorbed by the cotton terry towelling the baby's skin is kept damp. However, if a separate nappy liner made from a synthetic fibre such as Rhovyl or Tricel is used next to the skin under an absorbent terry nappy the skin is kept much drier. The urine wicks through the non-absorbent fibre layer and is held in the outer absorptive fibre. There is thus a hygienic advantage in using synthetic fibre fabrics near the damp skin.

THE DEVELOPMENT OF STATIC ELECTRICITY

Fabrics made from synthetic fibres, which absorb only small quantities of moisture, tend to produce an electrostatic charge due to friction when different layers of clothing rub together or against the body. This may cause some crackling or sparking, as can be seen when nylon underwear is removed in the dark. A nylon slip may tend to ride up in wear particularly if worn under another light-weight synthetic material. When using dress fabrics of low water absorbency such as nylons and polyesters, it is often advisable to use cotton or viscose linings as these are inherently non-static fibres and will prevent the cling or creeping of the outer fabric in wear. The relationship between static and soiling is not completely understood but it would appear that the effect is not as great as is often believed.

Antistatic agents are available, and when applied to synthetic fibres or yarns they decrease the accumulation of electrostatic charge. Nylons in which the antistatic properties are permanently built into the fibre have been developed.

The nylon polymer is modified by the introduction of additives which increase the electrical conductivity of the fibre.

It will be appreciated from this chapter as a whole that the subject of clothing physiology is not yet completely understood in all its aspects, but the above examples have perhaps illustrated that some of the traditional practices may have to be revised and new ideas accepted.

13. Labelling

WHEN a customer buys a textile article the choice will probably be largely based on the colour, appearance and style. However, one should also consider how it will perform in use, whether it is 'right for the job' and how it can be restored to cleanliness.

The many developments in the textile and related industries in recent years have now resulted in such a wide range of products that it is virtually impossible to know the answers to these questions merely by looking at the article, or even by knowing the fibre content.

In addition to the different types of man-made fibres available, new methods of mixing and blending them have been developed. Possibly inspired by the advance of man-made fibres, there are now many finishes for the natural fibres. Resin treatments can give minimum or easy-care properties to cotton shirts and shrink resistance and machine washability to wool. New colouring matters and the increasing use of spun-dyed yarns can give improved colour fastness and the applications such as foam and adhesive laminating can all alter the fabric properties.

There have also been corresponding advances in the related industries, with the increasing numbers of washing-machines, including automatics, spin-driers, tumbler-driers and coin-operated dry-cleaning units. The result is that the layman is no longer in a position to select the optimum treatment for cleaning an article, nor readily estimate exactly how an article will perform in wear.

It is therefore essential that this information shall be given to the customer, and with the many obvious problems involved in transmitting this verbally at the point of sale, the answer is in careful, accurate labelling, telling the customer exactly what he wishes to know, in a language that he can understand.

Any label which gives information is strictly an informative label but the subject can conveniently be divided into two sections. The first of these is care labelling, the function of which is to tell the housewife, and indeed the professional launderer or cleaner, the optimum treatment by which the article can most satisfactorily be restored to cleanliness. This information is obviously required throughout the life of the garment. Tie-on tickets are removed and easily lost and the most satisfactory method of providing care advice for textiles is on sew-in labels. Whether printed or woven, these should indicate clearly the recommended method, and remain legible throughout subsequent washing and cleaning treatments. Thus the information is permanently available.

The second group covers all labels which give the customer information about the article. These are most important at the point of sale and could help the customer to make a choice between similar products. This type of labelling is of particular value when purchasing larger, expensive articles which are designed to last a long time. A mistake made in choosing an item such as a carpet can be serious and the kind one cannot afford to make. Included in this group are brand-name labelling and quality-mark labelling, which, when backed by a reputable store or company, can give the purchaser a certain promise of value for money. Guarantees, fibre-content labels and those giving assurance of certain standards are also included in this section.

The different forms of labels can therefore be considered as follows:

(1) *Information of importance throughout the life of the article*
Care labelling – giving instruction for the optimum method of cleaning:
(a) in terms of short meaningful phrases,
(b) as symbols.

(2) *Information of importance principally at the point of purchase*
(a) fibre-content labelling,
(b) brand-name and quality-mark labelling, including guarantees and controlled standards,
(c) fully informative labelling.

CARE LABELLING

The simple advice needed for washing the fabrics made from natural fibres could be handed down from mother to daughter, and the average housewife had little difficulty in acquiring the necessary expertise on the subject. However, with the wide range of merchandise now available due to the introduction of new fibres and new techniques of dyeing and finishing, this is not possible. The consumer now rates the appearance retention of an article as important as soil removal. There is thus a requirement for positive instructions stating how the article shall be treated, rather than purely negative advice, such as 'do not dry-clean'. Many housewives now have at their disposal complex and expensive machinery, of which they wish to take full advantage – automatic washing-machines, spin-driers, tumbler-driers and laundrettes.

All these factors have led to a gradual realization of the need to give the consumer 'care advice'. Many textile manufacturers, makers-up, wholesalers and retailers began to introduce labels of this kind but these tended to be extremely elaborate or the manufacturer played very safe and gave the instructions 'wash by hand in lukewarm suds'. In some cases no doubt this was necessary, but in so many cases this represented merely caution on the part of the manufacturer. The poor housewife, however, had all her new equipment and wanted to make use of it.

An amusing example of a label attached to a swim-suit read:

> Contact with rough surfaces, finger-nails, rings, etc., or with chlorinated water should be avoided where possible. Rinse in fresh water after wearing to prevent any damage by suntan oils or body acids. Never put away damp. Always wash out gently in lukewarm suds, and rinse in clear water, avoiding detergents. Squeeze without twisting and dry by laying flat on a towel away from direct sunlight or artificial heat. Dyes are guaranteed fast to sunlight and sea water, but as some colours are less durable than others these hints should be observed for maximum garment life.

The labelling was also confusing because different people were using numerous terms to describe the different washing temperatures and the variations were endless. Many attempts were made to give the consumer better advice, and this was the aim of the codes introduced by different organizations; the Lux Washability Bureau, the Hoover Washability label, Courtaulds Care Labelling Code and the R.T.S.A. Wash–Clean Scheme. Although these schemes indicated the direction of development, they had varying degrees of success, but were not generally given the widespread support of all the related industries.

At this time the Molony Committee was set up to look into consumer affairs and its final report was published in 1962. This committee advocated the setting up of a national informative labelling scheme, which will be discussed later, and also made recommendations about care labelling. The committee recommended that the care instructions should be given on sew-in labels which would be permanently available and not on swing tickets. This is now generally accepted as the most satisfactory method of providing care advice. The report did not state a definite view on the question of care labelling by symbols as opposed to words. In order that the information can be given on a small label, which can then be sewn into the article in a suitable position where it will not be inconvenient or unsightly, it is necessary to use either short meaningful phrases or symbols. In Britain initial work was based on the use of short meaningful phrases, whereas some continental countries concentrated on the use of symbols. A system has now been devised for use in Britain using symbols, as described on the following pages, but retaining words in addition wherever feasible.

Before discussing in detail these different methods of giving care advice, it is necessary to consider the variables in any total laundering process.

The basic variables are:

   (i) the temperature of the water,
  (ii) the method of washing,
 (iii) the method of water extraction,
 (iv) the method of drying,
  (v) recommendations for ironing.

The recommended temperature of the water depends on the fibre properties, on the fabric structure, on the colour fastness and on the finishes applied to the fabric. Some cottons can be boiled, and other coloured cotton articles should be washed at 60°C or 40°C depending on the degree of colour fastness. Again, with white and coloured nylon the same factors affect the wash temperature. Other fibres such as the acrylics and wool need to be washed at lower temperatures of 40°C.

Different fibres and fabric structures require varying amounts of agitation; in washing-machines this is governed mainly by variations in the washing time. These times will vary with different machines depending on the severity of the process given by each machine. Certain fibres such as cotton require the maximum amount of agitation in order to obtain optimum cleanliness, whereas others such as the acrylics and wools require less agitation. Wool, in general, can present a problem if given too much agitation, since much movement in hot water would encourage shrinkage and 'thickening', known as felting, and thus the precautionary advice of 'do not rub' is applicable.

Again the recommended method of water extraction varies with different fibres. Hand-wringing and twisting may give permanent creasing to acetate fabrics and cause damage to wool articles. Necessary precautions must also be taken when removing excess water from thermoplastic fibres. If these are taken from hot water and crushed, as in a spin-drier, permanent creases may be set in. It is therefore essential to give all thermoplastic fibres a cold rinse prior to a short spin in order to avoid this. The method of drying may also need specifying in some cases. Certain articles may need to be drip-dried if the maximum benefit is to be gained from easy-care and minimum-iron finishes.

A manufacturer may wish to recommend that a heavy knitted sweater is dried flat in order to avoid the garment losing its shape. However, at this point it is worth mentioning that all care advice must be realistic in terms of what the housewife can be expected to do, or the value of the label is lost. For a drip-dry instruction to be appropriate, the garment must obviously be of the type that will dry quickly, because no one would want an article hanging in the house for three days! The term 'dry flat' is obviously not a popular one, since when this cannot be done outside, it can cause great inconvenience. Where possible, therefore, the consumer should be advised to remove the excess moisture by spinning or putting through a wringer and then line dry. The shape of the garment is often lost if the excess moisture is not removed before hanging to dry, and the weight of the water will distort the garment.

The optimum results with garments having the permanent press finish are obtained by tumbler-drying but the percentage of homes possessing tumbler-driers is at present not large in Britain and this type of drying is not generally possible, unless a laundrette is used.

The label must also inform the consumer of the correct iron setting to be used and give any specific advice necessary about the condition of the article for ironing. In order to get the creases out of a standard cotton shirt it must be ironed while still damp, but acrylic garments on the other hand must be ironed dry in order to avoid stretching. Different ironing temperatures will be required for different fibres and finishes. The cellulosic fibres require the higher settings to remove creases, unless given a special treatment, and will eventually scorch if the temperature is too great. The thermoplastic fibres, however, must be ironed at lower temperatures, which will remove the creases perfectly well. As the temperature is increased the fabric will begin to soften and eventually stick to the iron.

The acceptance of the need to give care advice is easy enough but devising a method of conveying all the necessary instructions simply and accurately on a small label is a more difficult matter. The first steps towards standardized care labelling in the U.K. came in 1966 when the Home Laundering Consultative Council, a working body of representatives from the major industries in this country concerned with the home washing of garments and textiles, published its Wash Code scheme. Before that date many companies in the textile, washing-machine and washing product industries were issuing their own laundry and care instructions but these varied greatly. For example, the terms warm, lukewarm and cool were used to describe the temperature of the washing water, and no one was quite sure what they meant. It became increasingly clear that some standardization was required and the Home Laundering Consultative Council was devised to meet this need. The members include representatives from fibre and textile manufacturers, detergent manufacturers, appliance manufacturers, and retail and wholesale interests.

The first achievement of the committee was agreement on washing temperatures and their description. This was followed by the development of an ironing test method and standardization of domestic iron settings and terminology.

In 1971 the scheme was developed into a complete British Care Labelling Scheme and at this time dry-cleaning instructions and dry-cleaning symbols were incorporated. The H.L.C.C. then negotiated with the International Care Labelling Symposium, the European care labelling body,* to devise a system which could achieve universal acceptance. Agreement on an International Code was reached in December 1973 and became effective in 1974 (Fig. 13.3).

The International Textile Care Labelling Code

The international Care Labelling Code is based on four symbols, each of which is variable. The outline symbols are given in Fig. 13.1.

Wash-tub:
The washing process

Iron: Ironing

Triangle:
Chlorine-bleaching

Circle: Dry-cleaning

Fig. 13.1   Care labelling symbols

1. Wash-tub symbol: The Washing Process

This indicates that the article can be washed safely either by machine or hand. The number above the waterline represents the full washing process and the figure below the waterline represents the water temperature. The symbol may be accompanied by a written description of the process. See Fig. 13.1.

A hand in the wash-tub indicates that the article must not be washed by machine. The appropriate hand-wash instructions, taken from the appropriate process, may be added in a box alongside the symbol.

When the wash-tub is crossed out as shown this indicates that the article must not be washed.

Fig. 13.2   Wash-tub symbol

There are nine numbered processes in the international code but only seven are likely to be used in the U.K. The full scheme is given in Fig. 13.3.

* Now known as GINETEX

MACHINE	HAND-WASH
1 / 95 Very hot to boil maximum wash	Hand-hot or boil
Spin or wring	

White cotton and linen articles without special finishes

MACHINE	HAND-WASH
2 / 60° Hot maximum wash	Hand-hot
Spin or wring	

Cotton, linen or viscose articles without special finishes where colours are fast at 60°C

MACHINE	HAND-WASH
3 / 60° Hot medium wash	Hand-hot
Cold rinse. Short spin or drip-dry	

White nylon; white polyester/cotton mixtures

MACHINE	HAND-WASH
4 / 50° Hand-hot medium wash	Hand-hot
Cold rinse. Short spin or drip-dry	

Coloured nylon; polyester; cotton and viscose articles with special finishes; acrylic cotton mixtures; coloured polyester/cotton mixtures

MACHINE	HAND-WASH
5 / 40° Warm medium wash	Warm
Spin or wring	

Cotton, linen or viscose articles where colours are fast at 40°C, but not at 60°C

MACHINE	HAND-WASH
6 / 40° Warm minimum wash	Warm
Cold rinse. Short spin. Do not wring	

Acrylics; acetate and triacelate, including mixtures with wool; polyester/wool blends

MACHINE	HAND-WASH
7 / 40° Warm minimum wash	Warm Do not rub
Spin. Do not hand wring	

MACHINE	HAND-WASH
8 / 30° Cool minimum wash	Cool
Cold rinse. Short spin. Do not wring	

Silk and printed acetate fabrics with colours not fast at 40°C

MACHINE	HAND-WASH
9 / 95° Very hot to boil maximum wash	Hand-hot or boil
Drip-dry	

Cotton articles with special finishes capable of being boiled but requiring drip-drying

	HAND-WASH

Articles which must not be machine-washed. Details will vary because garment manufacturers are free to put their own written instructions on this label

Do not wash

Fig. 13.3   International Textile Care Labelling Code. Examples of application

Machine Agitation   The amount of agitation is governed mainly by variations in the washing time, the descriptions used being maximum, medium and minimum wash. These times vary with different machines owing to the variation in the severity of the washing action.

Maximum wash means the maximum recommended agitation for any machine as defined by its manufacturer.

Medium wash means 40–60 per cent of the maximum recommended agitation.

Minimum wash means the recommended minimum account of agitation for any given machine, usually 20–30 per cent of maximum.

Washing Temperatures   Six different temperatures, including boiling, are used in the washing process, the temperature in degrees centigrade being shown in the wash-tub.

TABLE 13.1   WASHING TEMPERATURES

Temperature °C	Description	Consumer identification
100	Boil	Self-explanatory
95	Very hot	Water heated to near boiling-point
60	Hot	Hotter than the hand can bear. The temperature of water from many domestic hot taps
50	Hand-hot	As hot as the hand can bear
40	Warm	Pleasantly warm to the hand
30	Cool	Feels cool to the touch

Additional Information   Rinsing instructions are only included when they are of special significance. With the exception of 'Short spin' the instructions given for water extraction are self-explanatory. 'Short spin' is defined as the minimum spinning time recommended by the manufacturer of a particular appliance.

If required cautionary instructions may be added to the label, but these should be kept to a minimum. Typical examples of acceptable instructions are 'Dry flat' and 'Remove trimmings'.

2. Triangle: Chlorine-bleaching

This symbol indicates that the article may be treated with chlorine bleach.

If the symbol is crossed out as shown, this means that chlorine bleach must not be used.

Fig. 13.4   Chlorine-bleaching symbol

The symbol refers to chlorine bleach only and does not apply to other types of bleach. This symbol may appear on articles labelled on the Continent where chlorine bleaches are in more general use.

3. Iron: Ironing

There are four variations of the ironing symbol. The first three have dots to indicate variations in temperature. The temperatures given in brackets are the maximum sole-plate temperatures. The symbol crossed out indicates that the article should not be ironed, and should only be used in cases where ironing would be detrimental. It should not be used on easy-care fabrics to indicate that ironing is not necessary.

HOT (210°C)   Cotton, linen, viscose or modified viscose.

WARM (160°C) Polyester mixtures, wool.

COOL (120°C) Acrylic, nylon, acetate, triacetate, polyester.

DO NOT IRON. (This symbol should only be used in cases where ironing would be detrimental to the fabric and NOT on easy-care fabrics to indicate that ironing is not necessary.)

Fig. 13.5   Domestic iron settings

The types of fabrics likely to be ironed on each setting have been given, although it must be stressed that this is only a general guide. It is the responsibility of the textile manufacturer to assess which iron setting shall be recommended on a care label, and in the literature, for a particular fabric. In mixture fabrics the setting selected will normally be the one applicable to the fibre requiring the lower setting. Special finishes on a fabric might require that a lower setting be recommended than for the same fabric without the finish.

A basic test method has been evolved by the H.L.C.C. to enable the appropriate settings to be established.

4. Circle: Dry-cleaning

The circle, which refers to the dry-cleaning of an article, should never appear on its own but should always have additional information as given in Fig. 13.6.

 Normal goods dry-cleanable in all solvents.

 Normal goods dry-cleanable in perchloroethylene, white spirit, Solvent 113 and Solvent 11.

 Normal goods dry-cleanable in white spirit and Solvent 113.

 Do not dry-clean. The cross must be of the shape shown overlying the circle.

Fig. 13.6   Dry-cleaning symbols

In some countries underlined symbols, as shown in Fig. 13.7, are used where certain restrictions are necessary during the cleaning process. In certain cases it may be necessary to supplement these symbols with special instructions which may be given in words.

 Goods sensitive to dry-cleaning which may be cleaned with the same solvents shown for Ⓟ but with a strict limitation on the addition of water during cleaning and/or certain restrictions concerning mechanical action or drying temperature or both.

 Goods sensitive to dry-cleaning which may be cleaned with the same solvents shown for Ⓕ but with a strict limitation on the addition of water during cleaning and/or certain restrictions concerning mechanical action or drying temperature or both.

Fig. 13.7   Additional dry-cleaning symbols

5. Tumbler-drying Symbol

An additional symbol has been devised (Fig. 13.8) to indicate that a garment may be tumbler-dried. If the symbol is crossed out as shown then the garment must not be tumbler-dried.

Fig. 13.8   Tumbler-drying symbol

INFORMATION OF IMPORTANCE PRINCIPALLY AT THE POINT OF PURCHASE

The purpose of the second group of labels is to give the consumer information on such points as quality, suitability and performance in use. This is of great importance at the time of purchase. The customer is confronted with a wide range of products and has difficulty in deciding which particular article is most suited to his needs. When the cost involved is high and the article has to last a long time, like a carpet, how does the consumer know whether he is getting value for money? There are several different kinds of information given on labels and these will now be considered.

Brand-name and Quality-mark Labelling   Such labels should be used by a manufacturer or retailer on the grounds that he is proud of the brand or house name, which has become recognized, through long standing or much advertising, as a reputable name, associated with a reliable product. The advantages of these well-known brand names and house marks are great to the purchaser, who has a certain promise of value for money. At the other extreme, however, there are certain brand names or house marks which give no assurance at all and are associated with low-grade articles.

Certain quality marks are also used in the trade, and again their value varies a great deal. When backed by a reputable manufacturer, wholesaler or retailer the quality marks can be useful to the purchaser.

The 'Wool Mark' is used on approved articles containing pure new wool. Terylene-filled quilts are graded according to the weight per unit area of wadding and the different qualities are referred to as 'Red Label', 'Gold Label', etc. The various qualities of Slumberland beds are similarly referred to as 'Blue Label', 'Gold Label', etc.

Fibre-content Labelling   Fibre-content labelling is no substitute for care labelling, because it is impossible in the case of complicated blends for even experts to 'guess' at the appropriate optimum washing process. Small quantities of a fibre in a blend can also have varying effects upon the performance of that fabric, and the interpretation of this information in terms of the wear life of the article is impossible for the layman. However, in several countries fibre-content labelling is compulsory and can be of some help to the consumer. There are regulations governing fibre-content labelling which must be correct and not in any way misleading. If a fibre is named then there must be a minimum percentage of that fibre present, or the percentage given. Conversely a material cannot be labelled pure cotton if there is more than a certain small percentage of other matter present.

Labelling to Comply with Certain Standards

This type of labelling indicates that the goods have reached a certain quality standard and is of value where there can be a clearly defined minimum requirement, as when health or safety are concerned.

The British Standards Institute have produced certain standards controlling such things as purity of fillings in pillows and the performance of car seat-belts. In other cases, however, the consumer's needs will depend on the end-use, which means that the importance attached to the various characteristics will vary. For example, an acceptable resistance to abrasion for a spare-bedroom carpet would be much below that required for a living-room and the degree of colour fastness necessary depends on the location. In these instances and in appraising goods above or below the standard, the quality mark gives no assistance.

Informative Labelling

People have different requirements and thus a product that is suitable for one person will not be suitable for another. An informative label should give impartial facts and performance information about a product so as to help the consumer decide which article is most suitable for his needs. When a customer is selecting an article he has to consider the following points: performance, aesthetic appeal and cost. The price is readily available and aesthetic appeal is a personal assessment, but information on performance has rarely been available in the past. The Consumer Council when in existence introduced the Teltag Informative Labelling Scheme which aimed to provide just such information. However, since this body is no longer in existence it rests once again with the manufacturers to provide these informative labels or literature with their products.

14. The Making-up of Garments

THE introduction of the synthetic fibres has given new opportunities for variety in garment production. New styles of fabric have been introduced successfully into the mass market as washable materials, when in the past such fabrics, if made from the traditional fibres, were not serviceable. This increase in the number of washable fabrics has been possible because of the increased strength, the improved colour fastness and launderability, and the quick-drying properties of satisfactorily constructed fabrics. However, if full advantage is to be taken of these developments the correct techniques must be employed in making-up the garment. It is not within the scope of this book to cover extensively the subject of garment manufacture, but it is intended to discuss briefly the main topics.

CHOICE OF LININGS AND ACCESSORIES

Having selected a material that is suitable for the required end-use, care must be taken in choosing the components. One of the main features of the new fabrics is their washability, and it is therefore important that garments made from these should contain only washable components, including belts, pocketings, shoulder pads, etc. Washable buttons are also necessary, because a garment from which the buttons must be removed before washing cannot be classed as easy-care. Although fully washable, garments may frequently be dry-cleaned and care should be taken to ensure that belts, buttons and artificial leather trimmings can also withstand the normal methods of dry-cleaning. If this is not the case, then the purchaser and cleaner should be clearly informed of this on a sew-in garment label. It is advisable for the home-dressmaker to make a record of the care requirements. Some stores provide sew-in labels with piece goods, and these can then be sewn into the finished garment, as a permanent record. If these are not available a white tape marked with indelible ink will be adequate.

It is most important that all linings, interlinings and trimmings are of similar dimensional stability to the outer fabric under the normal conditions of laundering, pressing and domestic ironing. Differential shrinkage will result in unsightly cockling of the outer fabric. With washable materials fully shrunk or non-shrink trimmings should be used, and this applies to tapes and bindings as well as to linings, interlinings and sewing threads.

Linings and trimmings should have suitable durability and crease recovery for use with the outer fabric so that they will not limit the garment life. For example, a drip-dry, non-iron jersey dress should be lined with an easy-care fabric. The expected wear life must be considered when selecting pocket linings, that must withstand hard wear.

Interlinings

Stiffness and bulk are largely a matter of personal taste, but are related to the weight of the outer fabric. There is a wide selection of interlinings available including the traditional wovens and the newer non-woven bonded fibre interlinings such as Solena (Bonded Fibre Fabric Ltd) and Vilene (Bondina (Sales) Ltd). These bonded fibre interlinings can be used where previously scrim, cotton or linen interlinings, wool or hair canvas were used, i.e. in coat lapels and jacket fronts or as an underskirt to give body. They can also be used in conjunction with the more traditional materials. The properties of non-woven interlinings are discussed in some detail in Chapter 8. Interlinings are available with an adhesive coating, so that by heating and pressing the material can be fused to the outer fabric. These fusible interlinings save a considerable amount of work in the preparatory sewing operations.

Linings

The lining chosen must be of the correct weight and shade, with adequate strength. Unsatisfactory fabric performance leads to burst linings, seam slippage and other faults. Adequate seam allowances should be given with correct seaming.

Tricel linings have the advantage of being drip-dry and easy-care. However, all synthetic fabrics have low values of moisture absorption and may develop static electricity, which can cause the lining to ride up, particularly if worn next to a nylon slip, also of low moisture absorbency. Some people prefer to use cotton lawn or viscose linings as these are non-static and will obviate the cling or creeping of the outer fabric in wear.

CUTTING OUT

Laying-Up

Care must be taken to ensure that the fabric is cut without tension. It is important that errors in laying are not compensated by fabric distortion in making-up, as this will result in mis-shapen garments that will be ill-fitting and unattractive. When making-up knitted fabrics the length direction, i.e. the direction in which the fabric has been knitted, should always run vertically.

Marking

Limestone and clay chalks are available and can be used for marking fabrics. Alternatively, tailor's tacks can be made or V-shapes cut outwards on the pattern pieces.

Cutting

For cutting all fabrics, particularly synthetics, it is essential to use a sharp cutting edge. For the home-dressmaker this will be shears or scissors.

SEWING

When garments are washable it is important that steps be taken to avoid fraying; depending on the fabric being worked, pinking, overedging or taping may be found necessary. Seam allowances should be at least 1.5 cm, particularly if the fabric is to be left with only a pinked or raw edge.

When using high-speed sewing-machines for certain thermoplastic fibres, the needle may become overheated and cause fusion during sewing. Very high sewing speeds may therefore have to be avoided on these fabrics. The condition of the needle is also most important. Undamaged, fine, sharp needles should be used to avoid mechanical damage to the yarns. The most important factors concerned in producing a good seam are: the choice of sewing thread, the needle size, the thread tension and the number of stitches per centimetre.

Choice of Sewing Thread During recent years sewing thread manufacturers have made great advances in producing the correct thread for the job. The use of fully shrunk sewing threads offers definite advantages. Certain specially designed threads are now available for specialized operations and when making-up dresses in synthetic materials a synthetic sewing thread is recommended. A general recommendation for light-weight dress fabric would be a 60's thread.

In commercial production it has been found that lubricating the sewing thread gives improved results. The sewing thread, as it runs through the needle at high speeds, creates friction and produces heat. With thermoplastic materials the heat thus produced is localized at the needle and during high-speed sewing can cause the sewing thread to melt. The idea of lubricating the thread is to aid its running through the needle.

A second problem arises when friction is produced as the needle is pushed in and out of the fabric at high speed. The heat thus generated can cause fusion in thermoplastic materials. In addition to the problem of fusion, a fabric can also be harmed when a damaged needle cuts the yarns in a fabric and causes stitching damage. The application of a lubricant to the sewing thread does perhaps, to a slight extent, lubricate the needle itself and reduce the friction produced when the needle penetrates the fabric. However, the only really practical way to avoid friction between the needle and the fabric is to lubricate the fabric itself, as lubricating the needle is impossible.

The use of thermoplastic threads is unlikely to create these problems when using domestic machines, as the sewing speeds are so much slower.

Needles Needles should be inspected to ensure that blunt or damaged ones are replaced, because these will cause more damage than using a needle that is too large. The smallest, finest size of needle, consistent with the size of thread and the material to be sewn, should be used. A general recommendation for home-dressmaking with the lighter-weight dress fabrics would be a 10–12 needle, with sizes 14–16 being suitable for heavier fabrics. These needle sizes are given in Singer sizes.

Ball-point needles are now available for domestic use and are recommended for critical materials such as light-weight woven fabrics, velvets, some nylon jerseys and elastic fabrics. The ball-point needle ensures a uniform penetration hole and avoids material damages. Skip-stitches will also be avoided.

Needles with a narrow wedge point are recommended for sewing leather, suede, leather substitutes and plastic materials. The special leather point needles facilitate the penetration of the material and procure a sufficiently large hole for the thread.

Machine Adjustments   In order to avoid unsightly puckering at the seams sewing-machine tensions should be kept as low as possible to give a balanced stitch of acceptable appearance. One good way to obtain this is to suspend the bobbin and bobbin case by the thread and then adjust the spring tension until the bobbin just falls under its own weight. The bobbin is then replaced in the machine and a sample seam stitched. The tension of the needle thread is then adjusted to give a balanced stitch. For jersey it is particularly important to ensure that the tension is kept to a minimum.

The pressure on the foot can be important and should be controlled, particularly when changing from a harder, heavier fabric to a softer filament fabric such as Tricel surah. The pressure on the foot should be as light as possible, being just enough to facilitate the positive feed of the fabric through the machine.

Size of Stitch   The number of stitches per inch will vary considerably according to the fabric construction, but an average setting would be 12–14 per inch. Very fine fabrics such as lawns and georgettes will require more stitches, something like 16 per inch. With knitted fabrics such as jersey, it may be necessary to reduce the number of stitches per inch to prevent fabric distortion.

Pressing and Finishing   To obtain the best results in the finished garment each seam should be pressed as it is made, before proceeding to the next step. If the seams have been pressed properly during making-up then the final pressing will produce a much more tailored-looking garment.

In general, mild conditions, a light steaming and pressing with a cool iron, are recommended for synthetic fabrics. Severe pressing can cause glazing and pressure marks on materials such as triacetates and acrylics. Acrylic fabrics should always be ironed dry or with very little steam, but steam irons are recommended for all hand-pressing work on garments containing Tricel. A damp cloth may be used to flatten seams and hems in other fabrics. The fabric should always be ironed on the reverse side where possible, with a resilient cladding on the ironing-board.

15. Identification of Fibres

THE complete analysis of complex textile blends requires the skill and materials of an experienced textile chemist. However, it is often useful for others to be able to find out what fibre is present in the fabric with which they have to work. It is, therefore, intended in this chapter to cover the simple identification tests, which can be carried out with the minimum of equipment, but which do give an indication of the type of fibre present.

All methods of identification of textiles depend on the variation in the different physical and chemical properties of fibres. The simpler tests are discussed below and the charts which follow summarize the reaction of the most common fibres.

THE BURNING TEST

This is one of the most important tests available and when used carefully it can give much useful information. The fibres, after separating from the fabric, should be advanced slowly towards a small flame and eventually held in it. Care should be taken to test the warp and weft separately as they may be of different fibres. As the fibres are advanced towards the flame, their behaviour should be carefully observed. Thermoplastic fibres such as nylons and acrylics will melt and shrink from the flame. It should be noted whether a hard bead forms. Other fibres such as cotton, viscose and wool will not melt and hence do not form a bead. They will, however, support combustion and continue to burn. In general the cellulosic fibres char and burn emitting a smell of burnt paper and leaving a grey flaky ash. The protein fibres such as wool also burn, but leave a black, easily powdered residue and emit a smell of burnt hair.

MICROSCOPIC EXAMINATION

The cross-sections of fibres are generally distinctive and can give an indication of the fibres present. The longitudinal view of fibres, as seen under the microscope, can also be informative. Only a summary of the tests will be given here, but the methods are clearly set out in *The Identification of Textile Fibres*, published by the Textile Institute.

Some cross-sections and longitudinal sections of fibres are summarized in Table 15.1 and illustrated in Figs. 15.1–15.9.

TABLE 15.1 CROSS-SECTIONS AND LONGITUDINAL VIEWS OF FIBRES

Fibre	Longitudinal view	Cross-section
Wool	Surface covered by scales therefore fibre is serrated	Circular or elliptical. Variable in diameter. If present, medulla is variable in size
Degummed cultivated silk	Fine fibres or filaments variable in diameter, smooth, sometimes flattened	Separated fibres triangular, rounded corners
Tussah silk (wild)	Flat irregular ribbons, usually separate, sometimes twisted and with longitudinal striations	Very elongated triangles, usually separate
Cotton	Flattened and ribbon-like, with convolutions	Flat elongated or kidney-shaped with lumen. Seen as a line parallel to the longer direction
Mercerized cotton	Few convolutions	Most fibres have almost circular section with lumen small or absent
Viscose	Axial striations due to the serrated shape	Irregularly shaped with a number of serrations or lobes with fairly deep indentations between them
Polynosic fibres like Vincel		Almost circular
Acetate and triacetate fibres	Continuous striations running parallel to the edges of the fibres	Lobed, but lobes on each section fewer than for viscose
Nylon*	Uniform cylindrical shape	Circular sections characteristic of melt-spun fibres. Pigment delustrant particles may be present
Acrylics: Courtelle Orlon Acrilan	Uniform cylindrical shape	Differs according to type, four well-defined shapes are peanut, bean shaped, nearly round and lobed
Polyesters*	Uniform cylindrical shape	Circular sections

*N.B. Fibre variants include nylon with trilobal cross-section and polyester with octalobal cross-section.

SOLUBILITY AND SWELLING

The basis of these tests is the observation of the reaction of a fibre when treated with a chemical. The tests can be carried out by treating the fibres in a test-tube, but more information is obtained if the fibres are treated on a slide and the action seen through a microscope. Characteristic phenomena can then be observed. For example, some fibres can be seen to disintegrate and dissolve rapidly, whereas others swell in the chemical and may or may not dissolve.

A complete scheme of analysis for textile materials is given by the Textile Institute in their publication, *Identification of Textile Materials*, reprinted here as Table 15.2.

TABLE 15.2   CHART FOR IDENTIFICATION OF TEXTILES*

Grouping reagents	Time in min.	FIBRE	70% v/v acetone	Glacial acetic acid	4.4 N hydro-chloric acid Sp. Gr. 1.075	40% w/w sul-phuric acid Sp. Gr. 1.275	5 N hydro-chloric acid Sp. Gr. 1.085	Trypsin test 40° C	1 (sodi hyd id B
Fibre soluble in 0.25% sodium carbonate at the boil	1	Calcium alginate						sol.	ve slo s(
	4	Secondary cellulose acetate	SOL. 1 min	sol.					sap fi
	15	Cellulose triacetate		SOL. 4 min					
Fibres soluble in calcium chloride: 90% formic acid 1:10	½	Nylon 6			SOL. 2 min	sol.	sol.		
	½	Nylon 6.6				SOL. 2 min	sol.		
	6	Polyvinyl alcohol					SOL. 5 min		
	4	Bombyx silk							slo s(
	2	Casein						SOL. 15 min	
Fibres soluble in N sodium hypochlorite + 3% sodium hydroxide	3	Wool							S(18
	2	Ardil							
	5	Tussah silk							
	5	Vicara							
	½	Nylon 11							
	2	Polyacrylonitrile							
Fibres soluble in conc. sulphuric acid	5	Regenerated cellulose							
	8	Bleached cotton							
	10	Acetylated cotton							
	2	Polyethylene terephthalate							
Fibres insoluble in conc. sulphuric acid		Chlorinated polyvinyl chloride Polyethylene							
		Copolymer of vinyl chloride – vinyl acetate Polyvinyl chloride							
		Copolymer of vinyl chloride – acrylonitrile Copolymer of vinylidene chloride – vinyl chloride Polytetrafluoro-ethylene							

*By

0.25 N sodium hypochlorite	Meta-cresol	Conc. nitric acid	59% sulphuric acid 45° C	Cuprammonium hydroxide	75% w/w sulphuric acid Sp. Gr. 1.67	Xylol	Carbon tetrachloride Boil	Chloroform	Tetrahydrofurane	Acetone	Xylol Boil	
			partly sol.		sol.							**1**
	sol.	sol.	sol.		sol.				sol.	sol.		
	sol.	sol.	sol.		sol.			sol.		partly sol.		
	sol.	sol.	sol.		sol.							**2**
	sol.	sol.	sol.		sol.							
		sol.	sol.		sol.							
sol.		sol.	sol.	sol.	sol.							
sol.												
sol.												
sol.												**3**
SOL. 15 min			sol.	sol.								
	SOL. 3 min		gels		gels							
		SOL. 3 min			sol.							
			SOL. 7 min	sol.	sol.							
				SOL. 15 min	sol.							**4**
					SOL. 20 min							
					SOL. 5 min					sol.	sol.	
						SOL. 2 min					sol.	
							SOL. ½ min			sol.	sol.	**5**
								SOL. 1 min		partly sol. SOL. 5 min	sol.	
											SOL. 3 min	

Fig. 15.1   Longitudinal view of wool fibre (magnification × 300)

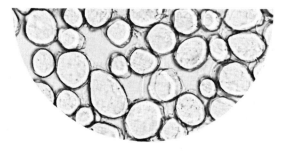

Fig. 15.2   Cross-section of wool (magnification × 500)

Certain fibres give characteristic reactions with specific chemicals and these simpler tests can be used in identification.

Viscose and Cotton   The cellulosic fibres are generally soluble in cuprammonium hydroxide solution unless they have been given a crease-resistant finish using a synthetic resin. Scoured cotton and viscose without a finish will dissolve completely in the cuprammonium, leaving little or no residue. However, acetylated cotton and cotton with aminoformaldehyde finish remains undissolved. Viscose fibres with a similar finish may swell but the fibres do not dissolve.

Crease-resistant regenerated cellulose can be confirmed by hydrolysing the fibres with 5 per cent sulphuric acid solutions. Hydrolysis may be carried out on a few fibres in a test-tube at a temperature near the boil for two minutes. A few drops of the sulphuric acid extract are then added to a solution of carbazole in concentrated sulphuric acid which has previously been prepared on a white spotting tile. A pale green-blue or deep coloration indicates the presence of formaldehyde, which is the most common constituent of many crease-resistant and stabilizing finishes.

A simple test for distinguishing between standard viscose and the chemically crimped viscose is to add normal sodium hydroxide to a single fibre on a watch-glass, and view this against a dark background. Chemically crimped viscose (Sarille and Evlan) will coil immediately, whereas standard viscose stays straight.

Dicel and Tricel   Two solvents can be used to distinguish between Dicel and Tricel.

Dicel is soluble in 70 per cent acetone solution but Tricel is insoluble.

Tricel is soluble in methylene chloride but Dicel is insoluble.

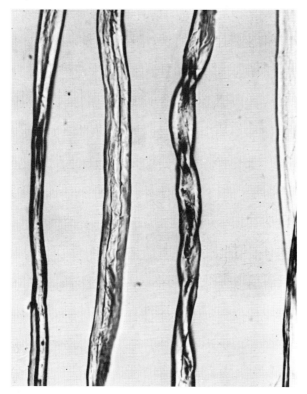

Fig. 15.3   Longitudinal view of cotton fibre (magnification × 300)

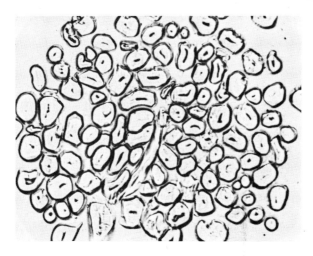

Fig. 15.4   Cross-section of cotton (magnification × 500)

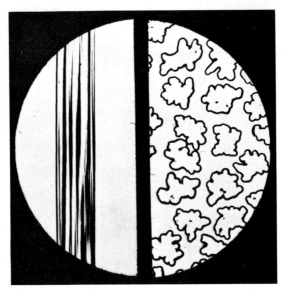

Fig. 15.5   Longitudinal view and cross-section of bright viscose (magnification × 500)

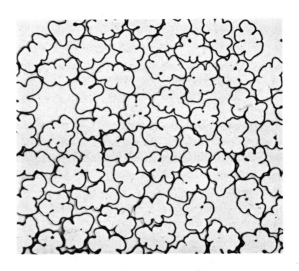

Fig. 15.6   Cross-section of triacetate fibre (magnification × 500)

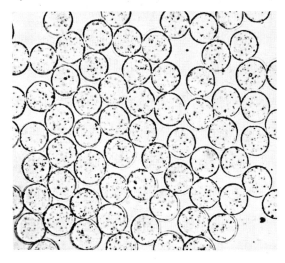

Fig. 15.7   Cross-section of nylon fibres (magnification × 500)

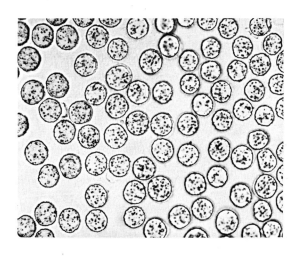

Fig. 15.8   Cross-section of acrylic fibres (magnification × 500)

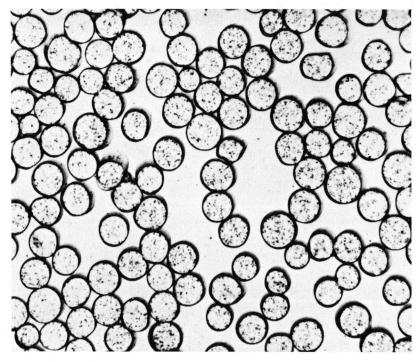

Fig. 15.9 Cross-section of polyester fibres (magnification × 500)

Standard viscose is insoluble in both of these reagents.

Acrylics The acrylic fibres are resistant to most chemicals and solvents but are soluble in dimethylformamide at 60°C.

To Distinguish between Nylons and Acrylics The polyamides dissolve in *m*-cresol but the acrylics do not.

Polyesters The polyester fibres are insoluble in 75 per cent sulphuric acid whereas the other thermoplastic fibres, except the chlorinated fibres and polyethylene, are soluble.

STAINING TESTS

Staining tests are valuable when undyed and untreated fibres are available, but they are of limited value when examining dyed fabric and garments.

The fibres should be wetted thoroughly, washed free from any wetting agent, and then placed in the stain at room temperature, for one minute. The specimen is then washed in cold water and examined for colour.

Shirlastain produce a range of different stains for this purpose. One frequently used product is Shirlastain A, and some characteristic colours for this stain are given in Table 15.3.

TABLE 15.3 STAINING TESTS WITH SHIRLASTAIN A

Fibre	Colour with Shirlastain A
Cotton	Pale purple
Mercerized cotton	Mauve
Wool	Yellow
Raw silk	Dark brown
Viscose	Bright pink
Cellulose acetate	Greenish-yellow
Cellulose triacetate	Off-white
Nylon	Cream to yellow (hot test, copper brown)
Acrylics	Unstained in cold

It is recommended that some known samples of fibres are examined initially in order to gain some experience before testing unknowns. Without these comparisons it is difficult to recognize the characteristics of the various fibres, particularly with regard to examinations carried out under the microscope.

Glossary of Textile Terms Used in the Text

Acetate   Fibres and filaments of cellulose acetate wherein less than 92 per cent but at least 74 per cent of the hydroxyl groups are acetylated.

Acetylation   The process by which an acetyl radical is introduced into an organic molecule.

Acid dye   An anionic dye, usually applied from an acid solution. Acid dyes have an affinity for wool.

Acrylic   A generic term used to cover a fibre manufactured from a long-chain synthetic polymer composed of at least 85 per cent by weight acrylonitrile units.

Air bulking   A mechanical process for producing a bulked yarn. The yarn is over-fed into a jet of compressed air, and this causes the filaments to loop and curl.

Alginate   Fibres and filaments formed from a metallic salt of alginic acid, the natural polymer in certain seaweeds.

Amorphous region   An area in a fibre where the molecules have been unable to arrange themselves in a regular manner, i.e. the less organized parts of a fibre.

Antistatic agent   A chemical which can prevent or reduce the generation of static electricity.

Antistatic nylon   Nylon with antistatic properties permanently built into the fibre by the chemical modification of the polymer.

Asbestos   A naturally occurring mineral of fibrous texture.

Azoic dyeing   The insoluble azoic dye is developed on the fibre by the combination of two components: the diazotized amine and a coupling component.

Basic dye   A cationic dye which combines with acids and can therefore dye wool, but now used principally for acrylics.

Batt   A carded lap of fibres.

Battiste   A fine, soft, plain-woven fabric, originally of linen.

Beam   A cylinder on to which a sheet of yarn or fabric is wound.

Beam dyeing   The dyeing of yarns and fabrics wound on to a perforated beam.

Beating-up   One of the basic motions involved in weaving. The inserted weft yarn is pushed up against the fell of the cloth by the reed.

Bleaching   Improving the whiteness of textile material by decolorizing it from the grey state.

Bleaching agent   A chemical reagent that will destroy the natural colouring matter of textiles, leaving them considerably lighter in colour.

Bonded-fibre fabric   A structure consisting of one or more webs or masses of fibres held together with a bonding material or by fusion.

Bouclé   A cloth with a rough surface produced by the use of fancy yarns. (The term is also used for relevant effect yarns.)

Box-spinning   A type of spinning in which a revolving cylindrical container is used, the package being built up in the inside of the container. (An early form of this device was known as the 'Topham Box'.)

Brocade   A figured fabric, in which the patterning is developed by floating certain threads. Used for evening wear and furnishings.

Bulked yarns   Yarns that have been treated physically or chemically so as to have a notably greater 'apparent volume'. Crimps, coils, loops or crinkles are permanently introduced into the straight filaments.

Cake   A package of continuous filament yarn produced during the box-spinning of viscose.

Calender   n   A machine in which heavy rollers rotate in contact.
            v   Fabric is passed through a calender to smooth and flatten it, to close the
            intersections between the yarns and to glaze the surface.
Calico   A generic term for plain cotton cloth heavier than muslin.
Carbonizing   A chemical process by which cellulosic matter is removed from a mixture
   with animal fibres. The cellulose material is degraded by treatment with acid, and may
   then be removed as a powder.
Carding   The reduction of an entangled mass of fibres to a filmy web by working between
   two closely spaced relatively moving surfaces clothed with points.
Cheese   A cylindrical package of yarn.
Chiffon   A light, sheer, open-mesh fabric in a plain weave.
Chlorination (of wool)   The reaction of the fibre with chlorine.
Cloqué   A fabric with a figured blister effect on the surface, brought about by the use of
   yarns of different character. These will respond in different ways to finishing treatments,
   for example two yarns of uneven shrinkage potentials are woven together. The fabric is
   then relaxed, one yarn shrinks more than the other and the excess material is left to form a
   design.
Combing   The process of straightening and parallelizing fibres and removing short fibres
   and impurities by using a comb.
Cone   A conical package of yarn.
Continuous filament yarn   A yarn composed of one or more filaments that run the whole
   length of the yarn.
Cop   A form of yarn package spun on a mule spindle.
Copolymer   A polymer formed from two or more starting monomers.
Corduroy   A weft-pile fabric in which the cut weft forms the surface, the binding points of
   the pile wefts being so arranged that once the pile has been cut cords or ribs are formed in
   the warp direction.
Cotton-spun   A term applied to staple yarn produced on machinery originally developed
   for processing cotton into yarn.
Count   A number indicating the size and thickness of a yarn, i.e. whether it is a coarse or
   fine yarn.
Course   A row of loops running across the width of a knitted fabric.
Crease resistance   The capacity of a textile material to resist and/or recover from creasing.
Crease-resist finish   A finishing process mainly for cellulosic fabrics, that gives increased
   recovery from creasing.
Crêpe   A fabric characterized by a crinkled or puckered surface.
Crimp   The waviness of a fibre or yarn.
Cross-dyeing   A dyeing operation in which one fibre in a mixture is dyed although the
   others remain substantially unchanged.
Crystalline areas   Those areas in a fibre where the molecules are regularly packed.
Damask   A figured fabric in which warp satin and weft sateen weaves interchange. Twill or
   other weaves are sometimes introduced.
Degree of crystallinity   The amount by weight, expressed as a percentage, of a linear
   polymer which is present in a crystalline form, the rest of the polymer being in an
   amorphous state.
Degree of orientation   The extent to which the fibre molecules lie in the direction of the
   fibre length.
Denier   The weight in grams of 9000 m of a filament or yarn.
Direct dye   An anionic dye applied from an aqueous dye bath containing a salt and widely
   used on cotton and viscose.
Disperse dye   Water-insoluble dyes usually applied as a finely divided dispersion. Originally introduced for dyeing cellulose acetate, now used extensively for synthetic fibres.
Dobby   A mechanism attached to a loom for controlling the movement of the heald shafts.
Dope   A solution of a fibre forming polymer ready for extruding through a spinneret, i.e.
   the spinning-solution.
Doubling   Feeding a number of slivers, rovings etc., into a machine and drafting into a
   single end.

Drafting Attenuating or increasing the length per unit weight of slivers, rovings, etc.

Drawing The operation of blending slivers, levelling them and drafting them to form rovings.

Dry spinning The process of extruding a solution of a polymer through a spinneret into a heated chamber. The solvent evaporates leaving the solid filaments.

Dye A substance which can be applied to a material and brings about a permanent change in the original colour of that material.

Edge crimping The bulking of a yarn by the introduction of coils into the filaments, as a result of drawing the heated yarn over a knife-edge.

Effect yarn Yarns inserted in a fabric to form a surface effect or enhance a pattern.

Elastane Elastofibre composed of at least 85 per cent of a segmented polyurethane, and which, when stretched to three times its original length and released, recovers rapidly and substantially to its initial length.

Elastodiene Elastofibre composed of natural or synthetic polyisoprene, or composed of one or more dienes polymerized with or without one or more vinyl monomers, and which, when stretched to three times its original length and released, recovers rapidly and substantially to its initial length.

Emboss To produce a pattern on a fabric by passing it through a calender in which a heated roller engraved with a pattern is run against a softer roller.

End An individual warp strand.

Epitropic fibres Fibres in which fine particles of carbon are embedded in the surface to give good electrical conductivity. At present nylon and polyester are available in epitropic form produced by I.C.I. Fibres Ltd.

Extrude To force a spinning-solution through the holes of a spinneret at a controlled rate.

False-twist crimping A method of bulking a yarn. Each section of yarn is twisted, set and untwisted, so that loops are introduced into the filament.

Fancy yarns A yarn which differs from the normal construction due to irregularities produced in it.

Fell (of cloth) The edge of the cloth in the loom, marked by the last weft thread that is nearest to the reed whilst the fabric is being woven.

Felt A textile in which the fibres are densely matted.

Felting The matting together of fibres during processing, wear or washing.

Fibre A unit of matter which possesses the properties of fineness, flexibility and a high ratio of length to thickness.

Filament A fibre of indefinite length.

Finishing The term used to cover all operations following bleaching, dyeing or printing, e.g. calendering, brushing, raising, starching.

Flame-proof fabric A fabric which does not propagate flame, i.e. any flame goes out quickly when the igniting flame is withdrawn, and which passes B.S. 3120.

Flame-resistant A flame-resistant fabric is defined as one which either will not burn, or will burn so slowly as to allow time to extinguish the flame or discard the burning fabric and thus obviate severe injury to the wearer. For test methods and performance requirements of flame-resistant fabrics see B.S. 5438 and B.S. 5722.

Flannel A fabric originally all-wool but now usually containing wool, in a plain or twill weave with a soft handle.

Flannelette A cotton cloth which has been raised on both sides to give an imitation of a wool flannel.

Flax Fibre extracted from plants of the species *Linum usitatissimum* used in linen fabrics.

Float A length of yarn on the face of a fabric between adjacent intersections.

Flock printing A way of decorating fabric. An adhesive is printed on the fabric and finely chopped fibres are applied all over. These adhere only to the printed areas and are mechanically removed from the other parts of the fabric.

Fully fashioned A term applied to knitted fabrics and garments in which the parts are shaped by widening and/or narrowing by loop transference to increase or decrease the number of wales. The pre-shaped pieces are subsequently stitched together to form a garment.

Grey fabric Fabrics as they leave the loom or knitting-machine.

Heald   A flat steel strip with an eye in the centre, or a similar device through which a warp yarn is threaded. Its movement can then be controlled during weaving.

Hessian   A plain cloth usually made from bast fibres, often jute.

Heterofil fibres   Original generic name for biconstituent fibres. I.C.I. Fibres Ltd produce nylon heterofil fibres with a sheath of nylon 6 and a core of nylon 66.

Jacquard   A patterning mechanism which gives individual control of up to several hundred warp threads on the loom. Large figured designs and complex patterns can thus be produced.

Jersey   A generic term applied to knitted fabrics.

Knit-de-knit   A bulked yarn of the crinkle type. Produced by knitting a thermoplastic yarn into a fabric, heat-setting and then unravelling.

Knitting   Forming a fabric by intermeshing loops of yarn.

Lace   A fabric consisting of sets of threads, some of which are twisted round the others at intervals, thus producing 'holes' as patterning.

Lap   In general, a sheet of fibres or cloth wrapped round a core, e.g. sheets of fibre wound on rollers after opening and cleaning.

Levelling   The migration of dye molecules resulting in more uniform distribution of the dye in the material.

Linen   Yarns and fabrics spun from flax fibres.

Linters   Fibres of very short staple length, which are removed from cotton seeds but are unsuitable for spinning.

Loom   A machine for weaving cloth by interlacing warp and weft threads.

Looming   The process of setting up the loom for weaving, i.e. drawing forward the warp yarns from the back beam through the eyes of the healds and through the dents of the reed.

Making-up   The conversion of fabrics into garments.

Man-made fibres   All fibres and filaments manufactured by man, as distinct from the naturally occurring fibres.

Marl   A marl yarn is produced by combining two slubbings or rovings of different colour or lustre.

Matt   Textiles where the normal lustre has been reduced.

Meldable fibres   Generic name for biconstituent fibres. I.C.I. Fibres Ltd produce nylon heterofil fibres with a sheath of nylon 6 and a core of nylon 66.

Melt spinning   The process of extruding the melted polymer through a spinneret into air or other gas or liquid, where it is cooled and the filaments solidified.

Mercerize   To treat cellulosic textiles with concentrated caustic alkali solution. This causes the fibres to swell, the strength and dye affinity is increased and the handle is modified.

Metallic yarns   Yarns containing metal. Several types are available, in one form a sheet of metal is coated with a film such as cellulose acetate butyrate or a polyester.

Modacrylic   Fibres produced from copolymers containing 50–85 per cent of acrylonitrile.

Modal   Regenerated cellulose fibre obtained by processes giving a high tenacity and high wet modulus. These fibres should be able to resist in the wet state a load of 22.5 g per tex. Under this load the elongation in the wet state should not be greater than 15 per cent.

Mule spinning   An intermittent method of spinning, now replaced by more modern methods in which the operations are carried out simultaneously.

Nap   A surface produced on a material in which part of the fibre is raised from the basic structure.

Needle   Instrument used for intermeshing loops in knitting. There is normally one needle for each wale. Also used for sewing.

Needle-bonded fabrics   Fabrics in which two or more webs of fibres are needled together. A batt of fibre is passed under, or between, barbed needles which pass up and down through the batt locking the fibres together.

Nylon   The generic name for the polyamide fibres.

Open-end spinning   The formation of yarn by separating the single fibres, which are then rotated and joined to the 'open-end' of the twisted yarn, which also rotates. Since there is a 'break' in the system any twist inserted is true twist.

Opening   The process of separating fibres from each other in the preparatory stages of spinning.

Pad-dyeing   Applying a dye liquor to textiles, either by passing the material through a bath and then squeezing out the excess with rollers, or by passing it between squeeze rollers, the bottom one of which carries the liquor paste.

Pick   The weft thread (or group of threads) laid across the warp during one revolution of the crankshaft of the loom.

Picking   Passing the weft thread through the warp shed during weaving.

Pile   A surface effect on a fabric produced by tufts or loops of yarn which stand up from the body of the fabric.

Pilling   The formation of tight balls of entangled fibres on the surface of the fabric.

Pirn   The package of weft yarn, of suitable size for placing in the shuttle of a loom.

Polyester   A synthetic polymer in which the chemical compounds used for its production are linked by ester linkages.

Polymer   A molecule of high molecular weight.

Polymerization   The combination or association of molecules to form a regular system of molecules, usually of high molecular weight, and known as the polymer.

Pressing   The heating of a material under moist or dry conditions to confer a desired shape, size or appearance on the article.

Printing   The application of dyes to the surface of a cloth, usually in specific localized areas.

Rayon   This generic term was originally used for regenerated cellulose fibres.

Reed   A device consisting of a number of closely set wires which may be used to separate and/or space the warp threads.

Relaxing   The releasing of strains and stresses in textile materials.

Retting   The separation of flax fibres from the other tissues in the stem by subjection to chemical or biological treatment.

Roving   The relatively fine fibrous strands used in the later processes of preparation for spinning. A sliver is drawn out to form a fine rope or roving which is then spun on the spinning-frame.

Sateen   A weave with weft floats on the surface, giving the fabric a rich lustre.

Satin   A weave with warp floats on the surface, giving the fabric a rich lustre.

Scouring   Treating textiles in aqueous or other solutions to remove fats, waxes, proteins, dirt, oil and other impurities.

Scrim   A generic term for a low-quality plain cloth of the muslin type.

Scroop   The sound characteristically associated with silk, which is heard when the fabric is compressed and rubbed together.

Selvedge   The longitudinal edges of a fabric formed during weaving.

Setting   The process by which stability is given to fibres, yarns or fabrics, usually by means of moist or dry heat.

Shantung   A plain-weave silk dress fabric using yarns which vary in thickness due to the irregularities in the yarn.

Sharkskin   A generic term describing fabrics with a stiff handle and firm construction.

Shedding   The raising and lowering of the warp threads to form a shed, through which the shuttle can pass, during weaving.

Shoddy   Wool recovered from fabrics in which the wool fibres are not matted together and can be separated out without too much damage.

Shuttle   A boat-shaped article which carries the weft supply package across the loom.

Single jersey   A weft-knitted fabric made on one set of needles.

Sizing   The application of a gelatinous film-forming substance, the size, to warps, generally before weaving. The purpose of the size is to provide a protective coating and prevent damage to the yarns during weaving.

Sliver   A thick, untwisted rope of fibres, which is the result of the carding process and is suitable for subsequent processing, i.e. combing and drawing.

Slub yarns   Yarns with short thick places occurring along the length.

Spinneret   A nozzle with holes or slits in it, through which the fibre-forming substance is extruded in the manufacture of man-made fibres.

Spinning   (1) This term is used to cover the process of drafting and twisting fibres in order to produce a yarn. The complete operation of the spinning-frame involves drawing out the roving, inserting the twist, and winding the twisted yarn on to a bobbin. (2) The term is also used to cover the process of extruding a fibre-forming substance through a spinneret, to form filaments. The word 'spinning' is therefore used to cover two distinctly different processes which should not be confused.

Spun-bonded   Non-woven materials in the form of sheets, tapes and laminates consisting of fine webs of randomly arranged continuous filaments.

Spun-dyed   Materials in which the colouring matter has been incorporated in the solution or dope before extrusion.

Spun yarn   Yarn produced from staple fibres held together by twist.

Staple fibre   Fibres of a suitable length for conversion into spun yarns.

Starch   A carbohydrate component of plants used in sizing, finishing and laundering.

Stenter/tenter   An open-width fabric-finishing machine used for adjusting the dimensions of fabrics, drying, heat-setting and fixing chemical finishes.

Stitch (knitting)   An intermeshed loop in a knitted fabric.

Stitch-bonded fabric   Fabrics produced by unconventional methods, other than weaving or knitting, in which: (a) yarns are stitched together, (b) a web of fibres is stitched.

Stretch yarn   A yarn capable of being stretched, but having rapid recovery on relaxation.

Stuffer-box crimping   The production of a bulked yarn, by packing the yarn into a small, heated box known as a stuffer box. The filaments are compressed into the limited volume and heat set with the zigzags in them. The resulting yarns have a typical angular crimp.

Taffeta   A plain-weave, closely woven, smooth and crisp fabric with a faint weft-way rib, produced from filament yarns.

Tenter   see *Stenter.*

Terry fabric   A warp-pile fabric with a pile in the form of loops, used for towelling, etc.

Tex   A system of measuring the fineness of yarns. Tex is the weight in grams of a kilometre. (Decitex = grams per 10 km.)

Thermoplastic   Able to be repeatedly deformed by the application of heat and pressure without any accompanying chemical change.

Top   The package of sliver that is the starting material for worsted and some other drawing systems.

Tow   A large number of filaments collected into a thick rope, which may subsequently be converted into staple fibre.

Tow-to-top conversion   The process by which the tow is cut or broken to form staple and then drafted into a sliver as a continuous process.

Triacetate   Cellulose acetate fibre wherein at least 92 per cent of the hydroxyl groups are acetylated.

Tweed   This term is now applied to fabric in a wide range of weights and qualities made from woollen yarns in various weaves and colour-woven effects.

Twill   A weave produced by varying the order of interlacing the yarns so that diagonal lines are produced on the face of the fabric.

Twist   The number of turns per unit length of yarn.

Velvet   A cut warp-pile fabric in which the cut ends of the fibres form the surface of the fabric.

Viscose   The solution obtained by dissolving cellulose xanthate in a dilute solution of caustic soda.

Viscose fibre   Regenerated cellulose fibre obtained by the viscose process for filament and discontinuous fibre.

Wadding   A loose mass of teased fibre used for padding, filling, etc.

Wale   A column of loops along the length of a knitted fabric.

Warp   (a) The lengthways threads in a woven fabric, (b) a number of threads in long lengths ready for weaving, knitting, sizing, etc.

Warping   The production of a sheet of parallel yarn in long lengths and evenly spaced.

Warp knitting   Making fabric by a method in which the loops made from each warp thread are formed mainly along the length of the fabric.

Weave   The manner of interlacing the warp and weft threads in a woven fabric.

Web   A wide film of fibres produced by a card or combing machine.

Weft   The widthways threads in a woven fabric, and yarn intended for use in this way.

Weft knitting   Making fabric by a method in which the loops made from each weft thread are formed mainly across the width of the fabric.

Weighting   The application of salts to a fabric in finishing, in order to increase the weight.

Wet spinning   The process of extruding a solution of a polymer through a spinneret into a coagulating medium, where the polymer is regenerated.

Winceyette   A light-weight fabric, raised on one or both sides and usually in a plain or twill weave, used chiefly for night wear.

Winch   A machine in which one or more endless lengths of fabric may be dyed.

Wool   The fibrous covering of the sheep.

Woollen   Description of yarns, fabrics or garments containing wool.

Woollen-spun   A term applied to staple yarn produced on machinery that was originally designed for processing wool into yarn.

Worsted   Yarn in which the fibres are reasonably parallel and which is spun from combed wool, or fabric manufactured from this type of yarn.

Worsted-spun   A term applied to staple yarn produced by systems originally designed for spinning worsted yarns.

Yarn   An assembly of substantial length with a relatively small cross-section, made from fibres or filaments.

Trade Marks Used in the Text

Acrilan   An acrylic fibre produced by Chemstrand Co., Division of Monsanto Chem. Ltd, U.S.A., and Chemstrand Ltd, U.K.

Acrilan SEF   A modacrylic fibre produced by Chemstrand Co., Division of Monsanto Chem. Ltd, U.S.A. and Chemstrand Ltd, U.K.

Agilon   A textured yarn produced by edge crimping. Process controlled jointly by British Nylon Spinners Ltd, U.K., and Deering Milliken Research Corp., U.S.A.

Antron   Trilobal nylon 66 fibre produced by E. I. du Pont de Nemours & Co. Inc., U.S.A.

Arnel   A triacetate fibre manufactured by Celanese Corp. of America.

Astralon C   A nylon yarn textured by the false-twist process. Controlled by Cheslene and Crepes, and Scragg.

Avisco Vinyon HH   A copolymer of vinyl chloride/vinyl acetate, produced by American Viscose Corp.

Ban-lon   A textured yarn produced by the stuffer-box method. The trade mark is used for fabrics or garments containing this textured yarn. Controlled by Joseph Bancroft & Sons Inc., U.S.A.

Blue C Nylon   A nylon 66 fibre produced by Chemstrand Ltd.

Bri-Nylon   A nylon 66 fibre. The trade mark is registered by I.C.I. Fibres Ltd, and is used on approved garments and fabrics made from their nylon 66 fibre.

Cambrelle   Meldable fibres and filaments used for making non-woven products manufactured by I.C.I. Fibres Ltd.

Celesta   A folded yarn of crimped Dicel with crimped polyester produced by British Celanese Ltd (Courtaulds Group).

Celon   A nylon 6 fibre produced by the Courtaulds Group.

Celon Antistat   A nylon 6 yarn with built-in antistatic properties produced by the Courtaulds Group.

Corfam   A non-woven synthetic material suitable for shoe uppers and linings and other applications, manufactured by du Pont Ltd (not now in production).

Counterstat   A nylon 66 yarn with built-in antistatic properties produced by I.C.I. Fibres Ltd.

Courlene   A polyethylene fibre produced by British Celanese Ltd (Courtaulds Group).

Cournova   A polypropylene slit-film yarn formerly produced by British Celanese Ltd (Courtaulds Group).

Courtelle   An acrylic fibre produced by the Courtaulds Group.

Creslan   An acrylic fibre produced by American Cyanamid Co. Fibres Division.

Crimplene   Formerly used for Terylene filament bulked yarn produced by a process developed by I.C.I. Ltd, now sold as bulked Terylene.

Dacron   A polyester fibre produced by E. I. du Pont de Nemours and Co. Inc.

Dicel   An acetate yarn produced by British Celanese Ltd (Courtaulds Group).

Dicel KN   An acetate yarn with latent crimp to give fullness and improved crease resistance in fabrics. Produced by British Celanese Ltd (Courtaulds Group). Not now in production.

Dielmoth Process   A method of producing a durable moth-proof finish by means of the chemical Dieldrin, produced by Shell Chemical Co. Ltd, U.K.

Dralon   An acrylic fibre produced by Farbenfabriken Bayer A.G., West Germany.

Durafil   A high-tenacity modified viscose staple fibre formerly produced by the Courtaulds Group.

Dynel   A modacrylic fibre produced by Union Carbide Corp.

Enka-Comfort   A nylon 6 yarn with built-in antistatic properties produced by British Enkalon Ltd.

Enkalon   A nylon 6 fibre produced by A.K.U. Holland and British Enkalon Ltd.

Evlan   A crimped modified viscose with high abrasion resistance produced by Courtaulds Ltd.

Fiberglas   A glass fibre produced by Owens-Corning Fiberglas Corp.

Fiberwoven   The trade mark used by Chas. Early and Marriot (Witney) Ltd for their blankets produced by the needle-bonding technique.

Fibro   Viscose staple produced by the Courtaulds Group.

Fibrolane   A protein fibre, formerly manufactured by Courtaulds Ltd (not now in production).

Floccal   A viscose fibre produced by Courtaulds S.A., France.

Floxan   A viscose fibre produced by Glanzstoff A.G., West Germany.

Fluflene   Polyester yarns, textured by the process controlled by Fluflon Ltd, U.K.

Helanca   A stretch yarn of the twist-untwist or false-twist type. Controlled by Heberlein & Co. Ltd, Switzerland.

Helion   A nylon 6 fibre produced by Chatillon S.A., Italy.

Kanekaron   A modacrylic fibre produced by Kanegafuchi Spinning Co. Ltd, Japan.

Koplon   A modal fibre produced by Snia Viscosa Ltd.

Koratron   A technique for giving a permanent shape to clothes containing cellulose fibres. Controlled by Koratron Technique (U.K.) Ltd.

Lanital   A protein fibre formerly produced by Les Textiles Nouveaux, Belgium (not now in production).

Lenzing 333   A modal fibre produced by Lenzing Ltd.

Lilion   A nylon 6 fibre produced by Snia Viscosa, Italy.

Lirelle   A polyester fibre produced by the Courtaulds Group.

Lurex   A metallic yarn produced by Dow Chemical Co., U.S.A.

Lycra   A synthetic elastofibre (polyurethane), for use in foundation garments and many stretch applications, manufactured by du Pont, U.S.A.

Merinova   A protein fibre produced by Snia Viscosa, Italy.

Metlon   A metallic yarn produced by Metlon Corp., U.S.A.

Mewlon   A polyvinyl alcohol fibre produced by Nichibo Co., Japan.

Miralon   A textured yarn (polyamide) produced by Heathcoat Yarns and Fibres Ltd, U.K.

Movil   A polyvinyl chloride fibre produced by Polymer S.p.A., Italy.

Orlon   An acrylic fibre produced by E. I. du Pont de Nemours and associated companies.

Perlon   A nylon 6 fibre manufactured by member companies of the Perlon Warenzeichenverband e.V., West Germany.

Proban   A specific finish applied to fabrics in order to reduce their flammability. Controlled by Albright and Wilson and the Bradford Dyers Association.

Pyrovatex   An organic phosphorus compound for producing flame-retardant finishes on natural and regenerated cellulosic textiles. Manufactured by Ciba-Geigy Ltd.

Qiana   A modified polyamide fibre produced by E. I. du Pont de Nemours and associated companies.

Reemay   A spun-bonded polyester non-woven fabric manufactured by du Pont.

Rhonel   A triacetate fibre produced by Société Rhodiaceta S.A., France.

Rhovyl   A polyvinyl chloride fibre produced by Société Rhovyl S.A., France.

Rilsan   A nylon 11 fibre produced by Soc. Valentinoise d'Applications Textiles, France.

Saran   A polyvinylidene chloride fibre manufactured by Dow Chemical Co.

Sarille   A chemically crimped viscose staple produced by Courtaulds Ltd.

Sayelle   An Orlon bicomponent fibre manufactured by E. I. du Pont de Nemours Ltd and associated companies.

Scotchgard   A water-repellent finish based on fluoro-chemicals, controlled by the Minnesota Mining and Manufacturing Co. Ltd.

Si-tussa   A filament blend yarn of acetate and nylon produced by Novaceta.

Solena   A bonded fibre fabric manufactured by Bonded Fibre Fabric Ltd (Courtaulds Group).

Spanzelle A synthetic elastofibre (polyurethane) for use in foundation garments and many stretch applications, manufactured by Courtaulds Ltd.

Taslan Air-bulked yarns processed under licence from du Pont Ltd.

Teklan A modacrylic fibre produced by Courtaulds Ltd.

Tenasco HSR, Tenasco Super I, Tenasco Super II High-tenacity modified viscose filament yarns of various types. Produced by Courtaulds Ltd.

Tergal A polyester fibre produced by Société Rhodiaceta, France.

Terlenka A polyester fibre produced by A.K.U., Holland.

Terylene A polyester fibre produced by I.C.I. Fibres Ltd.

Trevira A polyester fibre manufactured by Farbwerke Hoechst A.G., West Germany.

Tricel A triacetate fibre produced by British Celanese Ltd (Courtaulds Group).

Tricelon A filament blend yarn of Tricel and Celon produced by British Celanese Ltd (Courtaulds Group).

Tycora A textured yarn produced by the stuffer-box process by Textured Yarns (England) Ltd, and Textured Yarn Co. Inc., U.S.A.

Tyvek A spun-bonded polyester non-woven fabric produced by du Pont Ltd.

Ulstron A polypropylene fibre formally produced by I.C.I. Fibres Ltd.

Ultron A nylon 66 yarn with built-in antistatic properties produced by Monsanto Ltd. (Originally launched under the name 22N).

Verel A modacrylic fibre manufactured by Eastman Chemical Products, U.S.A.

Verranne A glass fibre manufactured by Société du Verre Textile, France.

Vilene A bonded-fibre fabric manufactured by Bondina (Sales) Ltd.

Viloft A hollow fibre viscose staple produced by the Courtaulds Group.

Vincel A polynosic viscose fibre manufactured by Courtaulds Ltd.

Vyrene A synthetic elastofibre (polyurethane) manufactured by Lastex Yarn & U.S. Rubber Co.

Zantrel Z4 A modal fibre manufactured by American Enka Corp.

Index

Accessories, choice of 202
Acetate fibres 36
  end-uses
    clothing 176
    furnishings 181
    industrial 184
  formula 38
  history 36
  production 37
Acid dyes 143
Acids, effect of 168
Acrilan see Acrylic fibres
Acrylic fibres 48
  end-uses
    carpets and furnishings 178
    clothing 177
    industrial 184
  high-bulk 67
  production
    Acrilan and Orlon 50
    Courtelle 50
  various forms of 47
Adhesive bonding of fibrous webs 127
Agilon 73
Air bulking 70
Air-jet loom 94, 98
Alginate 51
Alkalis, effect of 168
Anti-felting treatments 167
Anti-shrink treatments 155
Antistatic agents 189
Antistatic nylons 161
Arachne fabric production 126, 130
Arachne fabric uses 133
Araloop 126
Asbestos 25
Atlas fabric (knitting) 110
Avisco Vinyon H. H. 52
Azoic dyes 144

Back-filling 153
Ban-lon process 73
Basic dyes 143
Bearded needle 112
Beetling 153
Bending-length 170

Bicomponent yarns 76
Blankets, fibres used 183
Bleaching 138
Blend 5
Block-printing 148
Blue C nylon see Nylon
Bobbin loader 95
Body and skin temperatures 186
Bonded-fibre fabric
  production 126, 127
  uses 128
Bonding 156
Brand-name labelling 199
Bri-Nylon see Nylon
Bulked yarns 70
  air bulking 70
  edge crimping 72
  false-twist process 73
  gear crimping 72
  knit-de-knit 71
  stuffer-box crimping 73
Burning test for fibre identification 206

Calendering 152
Cambrelle 79
Camel hair 23
Carbonizing 57
Carding 10, 58–59
Carding engine 58
Care labelling 192
Carpets, suitable fibres and blends 179
Cashmere 23
Cellulosic fibres 6
  cotton 7
  fibre structure 34
  viscose 30
Celon see Nylon
Celon Anti-stat see Antistatic nylons
Chatham machine 128
Chemical resistance of fibres 168
Chlorination 154
Chlorofibres 51
Chromophoric structure 142
Circular weaving 96
Clothing, fibres for end-use 173
Coloration 141

Colour, theory of 141
Combing 10, 60
Comfort in wear 186
Compound needle 113
Continuous filament yarn 1
Converter 65
Copper number 139
Corduroy 102
Corfam 128
Coronizing 53
Cotton 7
  acetylated cotton 12
  bleaching 138
  effect of chemicals 168
  end-uses
    clothing 174
    household linen 182
    soft furnishings 181
    towels 182
  heat sensitivity 164
  history 7
  mercerizing 12, 140
  processing 10, 56–68
  production 7
  scouring 137
  structure of fibre 11, 34
Cotton count 3
Count (yarn) 68
Counterstat *see* Antistatic nylons
Courlene 54
Cournova 225
Courtelle *see* Acrylic fibres
Crease recovery 170
Crease-resistant finishes 155
Crimplene 225
Cross-sections of fibres 207
Curtain fabrics 181
Cut-and-sew garments 114
Cutting-out 203

Dacron *see* Polyester fibres
Damask 102
Denier 3
Design repeat 92
Desizing 137
Diazo compounds 144
Dicel *see* Acetate fibres
Dielmoth process 155
Direct dyes 143
Discharge-printing 149
Disperse dyes 143
Disposables 127
Dobby mechanism 92
Dope-dyeing 145
Doubling 62
Drafting 61

Dralon *see* Acrylic fibres
Drape of fabrics 170
Draw-frame 61
Drawing 10, 61
Dry-cleaning solvents 169
Dyeing 143
Dyes 142

Edge crimping 72
Effect yarns 70, 76
Elastanes, general 52
  end-uses 178
Elasticity 159
Embossing 154
Enka-Comfort *see* Antistatic nylons
Enkalon *see* Nylon
Epitropic fibres 78
Exhaustion dyeing 145
Extensibility 158
Extract 18

Fabric distortion 162, 167
Fabric manufacture
  knitting 103
  unconventional methods 126
  weaving 89
False-twist process 73
Fashion fabrics 173
Fashioning 113
Feel of fabrics 170, 187
Fell of cloth 89
Felt 81
Felting shrinkage 166
Fiberwoven 126, 128
Fibre-content labelling 200
Fibre dimensions 157
Fibre manufacture 26
Fibre sections 206
Fibre shape 1
Fibre strength 158
Fibre structure 2, 28
Fibres
  generic groups 3
  world production of 3, 5
Fibrolane 55
Filament blend yarn 77
Finishing 152
Flame-proofing 156
Flame-resistance rating 171
Flammability 170
Flat filaments 78
Flax
  fibre structure 14
  history 13
  production 13
  retting 13

Flexural rigidity 170
Float stitch 107
Fluidity measurements 139
Fully fashioned garment production 113

Gear crimping 72
Gigging 154
Ginning 9
Glass fibres 53

Hair fibres 17
Handle of fabrics 170
Heat, effect of 164
Heat-setting 154
Held stitch (knitting) 107, 108
Hemp 15
Heterofil fibres 78
High-bulk acrylics 67
High tenacity viscose 34
Home Laundering Consultative Council,
    labelling scheme 194
Hopsack weave 99
Household linen 182
Hypochlorite as a bleach 138

Identification of fibres 206
Industrial uses of fibres 184
Informative labelling 200
Insect attack on fibres 169
Interlinings 127, 203
Iron settings and terminology 198

Jacquard (knitting) 108
Jacquard loom (weaving) 92
Jet-dyeing 146
Jig-dyeing 146
Jigging 152
Jute 15

Kanekaron 226
Knapping 154
Knit-de-knit process 71
Knitting 103
Knitting constructions 103
Kraftamatic machine 134

Labelling 191
    according to standards 200
    care labelling 192
    informative labelling 199
Lace 81

Lace stitch (knitting) 108
Laminating 156
Lanital 55
Lansil 176
Latch needle 111
Latex backing 181
Laundering processes and variables 193
Levelling 145
Linen *see also* Flax 13
    end-uses
        flat woven towels and glass-cloths
        183
        household linen 182
Linings, choice of fabric 202, 203
Liquor ratio 145
Lirelle *see* Polyester fibres
Locknit 109
Longitudinal fibre sections 206
Looming 86
Lurex 54
Lycra 53, 178

Making-up garments 202
Malimo fabrics 126, 130
Malipol 126
Malivlies 126
Maliwatt 126
Marl yarns 76
Melamine-formaldehyde resin 155
Meldable fibres 78
Melt spinning 28
Mercerizing 140, 154
Merinova 55
Metallic fibres and yarns 54, 76
Methylene blue absorption 139
Mewlon 55
Micro-organisms, attack on fibres 169
Microscopic examination of fibres 206
Milling 154
Mixture fabric 5
Modacrylic fibres 54
Modal fibres 34
Mohair 22
Moisture absorption 160
Moisture, comfort factor 161, 188
Moisture regain 160
Mordants 143
Moth-proofing 155
Mungo 18

Natural fibres 6
    of animal origin 16
    of mineral origin 25
    of vegetable origin 6
Needle-bonded fabrics 126, 128

Needles (knitting) 111
Needles used for sewing 204
Noble combs 60
Non-woven fabrics 126
Nylon 41
  high tenacity 44
  history 41
  notation of types 42
  nylon 6 production 44
  nylon 66 production 42
  polymer structure 41
  uses
    for carpets 179
    for clothing 176
    for sheets 182
    industrial 184

Open-end spinning 63
Opening and mixing 57
Organic solvents, effect of 169
Orlon see Acrylic fibres
Oxidizing agents 168

Pacific converter 67
Packaging 84
Pad-dyeing 145
Parchmentizing 141
Perlon see Nylon
Permanent pleating 166
Picking 91
Pigment-printing 144
Pigments 144
Pile fabrics 102
Pilling 183
Plain knitting 103
Plain weave and variations 99
Polyamides see Nylon
Polyester fibres 44
  production of Terylene 46
  uses
    clothing 177
    curtaining 181
    industrial 184
Polynosic viscose 34
Polyolefin fibres 54
Polyurethanes 52
Polyvinyl alcohol fibres 55
Polyvinyl chloride fibres 51
Polyvinylidene chloride fibres 52
Poplin 100
Pressing see also Iron settings and ter-
  minology 205
Printing 148
Proban finish 156, 172
Processing of grey cloth 137

Properties of fibres, yarns and fabrics 157
Proteins 55
Purification 137
Purl knitting 107
Pyrovatex CP 156

Quality-mark labelling 199

Raising 154
Rapier loom 97
Rayon 30
Reactive dyes 144
Reemay 135
Relaxation shrinkage 155, 167
Repp 100
Resin finishes 155
Resist-dyeing 149
Retting 13
Rhovyl 52
Rib structure (knitting) 106
Ribbon filaments 78
Rilsan 42
Ring-spinning 63
Roller-printing 148
Rotating drum method of break-spinning
  65

Saran 52
Sarille 175
Sateen weave 101
Satin weave 101
Schreiner calendering 153
Scotchgard 156
Scouring 137
Screen-printing 148
Semi-hard floorings 180
Sewing 204
Sewing threads, choice of 204
Shedding (fibre loss) 183
Shedding (in weaving) 91
Shetland wool 18
Shoddy 18
Shrink resistance 155
Shrinkage 166
Shoe upper materials 128
Silk 23
  fibre structure 24
  history 23
  processing 24
  production 23
  spun 24
  uses 175
  weighting 24
Singeing 137

Sisal 16
Sizing 85
Skin wool 18
Slipe wool 18
Slub yarn 76
Snarl yarn 76
Softening 154
Solena 127, 203
Solubility of fibres 207
Sorption heat of clothing 188
Spanzelle 53, 178
Speciality yarns 76
Spectrum 142
Spin-dyeing 145
Spinning
   man-made production 26
   yarn formation 56, 62, 63
Split films for textiles 2
Spun-bonded fabrics 126, 134
Spun yarn 1
Staining, identification test 214
Starching 153
Static 161, 189
Stenter 152
Stentering 152
Stitch-bonded fabrics 126, 130
Stitch size 205
Strength of fibres and fabrics 158
Stuffer-box crimping 73
Sulzer shuttleless weaving machine 97
Swelling, means of identification 207
Swelling of fibres and yarns 162
Symbol labels 195
Synthetic polymers, history of develop-
   ment 41

Taslan yarn 70
Teklan 54, 171
Teltag Informative Labelling Scheme 201
Tenacity 158
Tenasco 34
Tensile strength 158
Tentering *see* Stentering
Terlenka *see* Polyester fibres
Terylene *see* Polyester fibres
Tex 3, 68
Textured yarn 70
Thermoplasticity 164
Towels, fibres used 182
Tow-to-top conversion 65
Trade marks 4, 225
Transfer-printing 150
Trevira *see* Polyester fibres
Triacetate fibres 40
   formula 38
   history 36

production 40
   uses 176
Tricel *see* Triacetate fibres
Tricelon 77
Tricot 109
Trilobal filaments 78
Tuck stitch 108
Turbo stapler 68
Twill weave 101
Twist (yarn) 69
Tyvek 135

Ulstron 227
Unifil loom winder 96
Upholstery fabrics 178, 180
Urea-formaldehyde resin 155
Uses of fibres 173

Vat dyes 144
Velvet and velveteen 102
Vilene 127, 203
Viloft 175
Vincel 36, 175
Vinylon 55
Vinyon 52
Viscose 30
   crimped fibres 34
   fibre structure 34
   high tenacity 34
   history 30
   low flammability fibre 172
   production, viscose process 30
   uses
      carpets, upholstery and soft furnish-
         ings 178
      clothing 175
      industrial 185

Warmth of fabrics 170, 187
Warping 84
Warp-knitted fabric constructions 109
Washing temperatures 193
Water (uptake by fibres) 160, 188
Water inhibition 160
Water-jet loom 94, 98
Water-proofing 156
Water-repellent fabrics 156
Water vapour uptake by fabrics 188
Weaves 99
Weaving 89
   conventional loom 89
   improvements to conventional loom 95
   new methods of weft insertion 95, 97
Weft-knitted fabrics 103

Weighting 24
Wet spinning 26
Wicking 189
Winch-dyeing 146
Winding 84
Wool 17
  bleaching 138
  carbonizing 19
  carding 19
  count 19
  different types 18
  disulphide linkages 22
  effect of chemicals 168
  end-uses
    blankets 183
    carpets and upholstery 178
    clothing 174
  felting 166

  fibre structure 20
  heat sensitivity 164
  history 17
  production and processing 18, 19
  salt linkages 22
  scouring 137
  woollen yarns 19
  worsted yarns 20
Wool mark 18, 200

Yarn manufacture 56
  carding 58
  combing 60
  drafting 61
  drawing 61
  preparatory processes 56
  spinning 62